Foundations for Algebra: Year 2

Managing Editors:

Elizabeth Coyner
  Bear River School
Beverly Brockhoff
  Glen Edwards Middle School

Illustrator:

Jonathan Weast
  Weast & Weast Illustration Studio
  Sacramento, California

Technical Assistance:

Bethany Sorbello
  CPM Educational Program
Thu Pham
  The CRESS Center
  University of California, Davis

Developed by CPM Educational Program

Program Directors:

Judith Kysh
  Departments of Mathematics and Education
  San Francisco State University
Tom Sallee
  Department of Mathematics
  University of California, Davis
Brian Hoey
  CPM Educational Program

v 3.0

THIS BOOK IS THE PROPERTY OF:

Book No._____

ISSUED TO	Year Used	CONDITION	
		ISSUED	RETURNED

PUPILS to whom this textbook is issued must not write on any page or mark any part of it in any way, unless otherwise instructed by the teacher.

Credits for the First Edition

Substantially Revised (2000, 2001)
by

Heidi Ackley	Judy Kysh
Steve Ackley	Kris Petersen
Elizabeth Baker	Robert Petersen
Bev Brockhoff	Edwin Reed
Ellen Cafferata	Stacy Rocklein
Elizabeth Coyner	Kristie Sallee
Sara Effenbeck	Tom Sallee
William Funkhouser	Howard Webb
Brian Hoey	Kaye Whitney
Carol Jancsi	Jon Wickham

Pilot Edition Contributing Editors (1999)

Heidi Ackley	William Funkhouser
Steve Ackley	Bruce Grip
Bev Brockhoff	Stephen Inouye
Ellen Cafferata	Carol Jancsi
Elizabeth Coyner	Alvin Mendle, Jr.
Scott Coyner	Pattie Montgomery
Kathleen Davies	Edwin Reed
Merci Del Rosario	Gail Standiford
Virginia Downing	Gale Sunderland
Sara Effenbeck	Howard Webb
Alice Elstien	Kaye Whitney
William Ford	Jon Wickham

Technical Assistance

Jennifer Buddenhagen	Jeremy Tauzer
Grace Chen	David Trombly
Ankit Jain	Erika Wallender
Janelle Petersen	Emily Wheelis

5 6 7 8 9 10 11 12   10 09 08 07 06   ISBN-10   1-931287-08-2

Printed in the United States of America Version 3.0 ISBN-13: 978-1-931287-08-1

Foundations for Algebra: Year 2

First Edition

Table of Contents

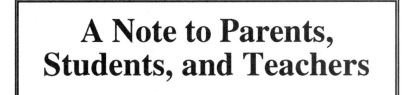

A Note to Parents, Students, and Teachers

Welcome to *Foundations for Algebra: Year 2.*

This textbook will prepare students for future Algebra courses. It was also written to consolidate the core ideas of previous mathematics courses, so that it will serve students of varied mathematics backgrounds. The contents of this course are many of the fundamental ideas and procedures necessary to be successful in subsequent mathematics courses and many careers. Classroom teachers wrote the lessons to present these ideas in ways that have proven successful with their students. The course also meets local, state, and national curriculum standards.

The investigations, problems, and practice exercises are designed to develop the students' logical and mathematical reasoning skills. The sequence of problems leads to understanding the reasoning behind the mathematical concepts. Students complete guided investigations that explore and develop ideas, then practice them along with procedural skills in subsequent chapters. Many problems use the mathematics in situations like those encountered by students and adults in their daily activities and business settings.

In order to be successful in mathematics it is critical that students actively participate in their learning. This means that each student must read and work all of the problems. Students need to discuss mathematical concepts and the reasoning involved in the steps of their solutions. In order to provide these discussion opportunities, students are encouraged to work with a study partner and in study teams both inside and outside the classroom. It is critical that students complete ALL of the assignments, including homework, to develop their individual skills. Equally important is that students take accurate, complete notes and ask questions about any problem, question, or concept that they find confusing or difficult to understand.

There are two additional resources that the authors designed to help students be successful in this course. The first is the mathematics Tool Kit that contains most of the ideas a student needs to know in the course. Tool Kit entries appear in the student text and in a Tool Kit booklet. The other is the *Foundations for Algebra Parent Guide.* The guide is sometimes available from the classroom teacher or the school library. It is available through the Internet at www.cpm.org. It may also be purchased directly from CPM Educational Program for $20 plus $3 shipping (California residents please add local sales tax to the $20) by sending a check to CPM, 1233 Noonan Drive, Sacramento, CA 95822.

Ray Sheo's
PRO-PORTION RANCH

Chapter 6

Chapter 6
Ray Sheo's Pro-Portion Ranch: **RATIOS AND PROPORTIONS**

In this chapter you will calculate the area and perimeter of rectangles, parallelograms, triangles, and trapezoids. You will also calculate the area and circumference of circles. You will enlarge and reduce these figures and study similarity. In your study of similarity, you will be introduced to proportions. You will learn to write proportions and solve problems using proportions. Writing and solving proportions are two very important and useful skills that will serve as a strong foundation as you continue in your study of mathematics.

In this chapter you will have the opportunity to:

- find the area of any parallelogram.
- find the area of any triangle.
- find the area of any trapezoid.
- find the area and circumference of any circle.
- reduce and enlarge figures.
- write ratios to compare items.
- write and solve proportions.
- use properties of similar figures and proportions to solve for unknown lengths, perimeters, and areas.
- use proportions to solve percentage problems.

Read the problem below, but **do not try to solve it now**. What you learn over the next few days will enable you to solve it.

RS-0. Ray Sheo, owner of the Pro-Portion Ranch, needs to build a bridge over the Roaring River that runs through his land. He has no idea how far it is across the river, but his daughter, Maria, knows she can find out by using the properties of similar triangles. Use the drawing at right and help Maria find the distance across the river.

Number Sense	
Algebra and Functions	
Mathematical Reasoning	
Measurement and Geometry	
Statistics, Data Analysis, & Probability	

Chapter 6
Ray Sheo's Pro-Portion Ranch: RATIOS AND PROPORTIONS

RS-1.

CONGRUENT

Two shapes (triangles, for example) are **CONGRUENT** if they have exactly the same size and shape.

Later in the chapter we will discuss similar figures (figures that have the same shape but not necessarily the same size).

Write the following notes to the right of the double-lined box in your Tool Kit.

Name two objects in the classroom that are congruent.

RS-2.

Felipé Sheo knew that he was 60 inches tall and that his sister Maria was 5 feet tall.

Felipé said, "Hey, I'm 12 times as tall as you, since 5 times 12 equals 60." At first Maria was puzzled, but then she said, "That's not true, and I know why."

Explain in a complete sentence what Maria realized.

RS-3.

RATIO

A **RATIO** is the comparison of two quantities by division. A ratio can be written as a fraction, in words, or with colon notation. (We will use the fraction form in this class.)

$$\frac{26 \text{ miles}}{1 \text{ gallon}} \qquad 26 \text{ miles to 1 gallon} \qquad 26 \text{ miles : 1 gallon}$$

A ratio: • should never be written as a mixed number.

• must have units labeled when the units are different.

Highlight the fraction form in your Tool Kit to emphasize that is how we will write ratios in this class.

RS-4.   The way a ratio is stated will tell you which value is written in the numerator and which one is in the denominator. For example, if you are comparing 65 miles to 1 hour, your values will be written as $\frac{65 \text{ miles}}{1 \text{ hour}}$. The units in a ratio help you remember the order in which to write it. If you are comparing the same kinds of things, you may omit the units. For example, if you are comparing 12 feet to 8 feet, you may write the ratio as $\frac{12}{8}$. Just as fractions can sometimes be simplified, sometimes ratios can also be simplified. For example, $\frac{12}{8}$ can be simplified to $\frac{3}{2}$. Use the Identity Property of Multiplication (Giant **1**) as necessary to simplify ratios.

a)   What is the ratio of 120 miles to 3 hours?

b)   Write a ratio comparing the time it takes to drive from Atlanta to Richmond (7 hours) to the time it takes to fly (1 hour).

c)   What is the ratio of girls to boys in this classroom today?

d)   Write the ratio of 6 feet to 9 feet.

e)   Write the ratio of 90 seconds to 20 seconds.

f)   Write the ratio of 17 days to 51 days.

RS-5.   Sometimes ratios involve hours and minutes–two different units of time–or feet and inches–two different units of distance. In such cases, we need to be sure the units are the same. For example, the ratio of 8 feet to 2 yards is the same as the ratio of 8 feet to 6 feet, since 2 yards equals 6 feet or $\frac{8}{6} = \frac{4}{3}$. Write the following ratios and simplify them if possible.

a)   What is the ratio of 2 hours to 180 minutes?

b)   What is the ratio of 6 inches to 3 feet?

c)   What is the ratio of four eggs to 12 eggs?

d)   What is the ratio of eight eggs to two dozen eggs?

RS-6.

PROPORTION

An equation stating that two ratios are equal is called a **PROPORTION**.

Examples: $\frac{2}{4} = \frac{3}{6}$, $\frac{5}{7} = \frac{50}{70}$, $\frac{154}{49} = \frac{44}{14}$

Write the following notes to the right of the double-lined box in your Tool Kit.

Explain in your own words what a proportion is. Include an example of a proportion.

RS-7. The sides of congruent figures that are arranged in similar ways in a figure are called corresponding sides. You may write ratios to compare the lengths of corresponding sides of figures. For example, in the two congruent triangles at right, side a corresponds to side d, side b to side e, and side c to side f. We can write the ratios $\frac{a}{d}$, $\frac{b}{e}$, and $\frac{c}{f}$.

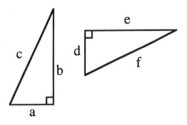

Be sure to keep the order in which you compare the corresponding sides consistent. In the above example, sides of the triangle on the left were compared to the sides of the triangle on the right. The short leg (left figure) matched the short leg (right figure), the long leg (left figure) matched the long leg (right figure), and so forth.

Complete the ratios below using the corresponding sides. Assume that the pairs of figures are congruent.

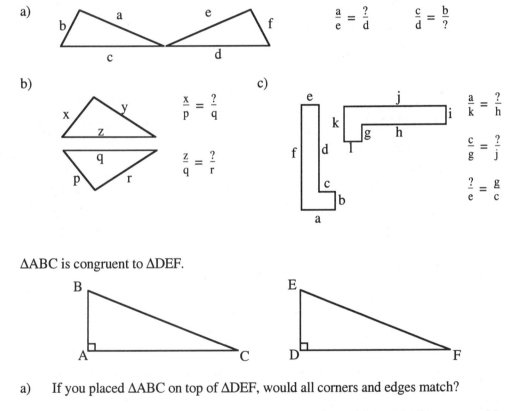

a)
$$\frac{a}{e} = \frac{?}{d} \qquad \frac{c}{d} = \frac{b}{?}$$

b)
$$\frac{x}{p} = \frac{?}{q}$$
$$\frac{z}{q} = \frac{?}{r}$$

c)
$$\frac{a}{k} = \frac{?}{h}$$
$$\frac{c}{g} = \frac{?}{j}$$
$$\frac{?}{e} = \frac{g}{c}$$

RS-8.   ΔABC is congruent to ΔDEF.

a)   If you placed ΔABC on top of ΔDEF, would all corners and edges match?

b)   Side AB and side DE are corresponding parts. These sides are in the same position in the triangles. Which side corresponds to side AC?

c)   Which side corresponds to side BC?

d)   Angle B and angle E are corresponding angles. Which angle corresponds to angle F?

e)   Which angle corresponds to angle D?

f)   In your own words, explain what corresponding means for sides and angles of figures.

RS-9. Jane had to find an equivalent fraction for $\frac{75}{80}$. What she wrote is shown at right. Decide with your partner whether or not Jane wrote a proportion. Explain.

$$\frac{75}{80} = \frac{15}{16}$$

RS-10. Find an equivalent fraction to complete each proportion below.

a) $\frac{6}{15} = —$

b) $\frac{13}{39} = —$

RS-11. Solve each equation.

a) $8n = 72$

b) $12e = 720$

c) $6.5y = 19.5$

d) $1.5k = 48$

e) $38t = 85.5$

f) $62w = 76.942$

RS-12. A five-pound box of sugar costs $1.80 and contains 12 cups of sugar. Marella and Mark are making a batch of cookies. The recipe calls for 2 cups of sugar. Determine how much the sugar for the cookies costs. Use a proportion to solve the problem. Show all your work.

RS-13. Complete the following table and graph the rule: $y = 3x - 2$.

x	-4	-3	-2	-1	0	1	2	3	4
y									

a) What is the x-intercept?

b) What is the y-intercept?

RS-14. Calculate.

a) $-60 \div 5$

b) $(-6) \cdot (-8)$

c) $6 - 17$

d) $-6 - 6$

e) $8 + (-13)$

f) $-14 - (-4)$

g) $-21 - 2$

h) $-12 + (-50) + 4$

i) $9 - (-17)$

RS-15. Now that we have started a new chapter, it is time for you to organize your binder.

a)   Put the work from the last chapter in order and keep it in a separate folder.

b)   When this is completed, write, "I have organized my binder."

RS-16. Follow your teacher's instructions for practicing mental math. What strategy did you use?

RS-17. You have used the Identity Property of Multiplication (Giant **1**) to find equivalent fractions and to solve proportions. Copy and compute the problems below. Show the values you used within the Giant **1**.

a) $\frac{7}{12} = \frac{56}{m}$ can be solved $\frac{7}{12} \cdot \boxed{-} = \frac{56}{m}$

b) $\frac{8}{3} = \frac{n}{48}$ can be solved $\frac{8}{3} \cdot \boxed{-} = \frac{n}{48}$

c) $\frac{20}{26} \cdot \boxed{-} = \frac{k}{39}$

d) $\frac{20}{42} \cdot \boxed{-} = \frac{50}{h}$

RS-18. Look at your work in the previous problem.

a)   How were the values used within the Giant **1** in parts (c) and (d) different from the values used in parts (a) and (b)?

b)   In part (d), how did you find the numbers in the Giant **1**? Explain.

RS-19. Solve each proportion using the Giant **1** in each problem.

a) $\frac{7}{12} = \frac{m}{18}$ can be solved $\frac{7}{12} \cdot \boxed{-} = \frac{m}{18}$

b) $\frac{5}{8} \cdot \boxed{-} = \frac{30}{n}$

c) $\frac{2}{3} \cdot \boxed{-} = \frac{w}{36}$

d) $\frac{4}{5} \cdot \boxed{-} = \frac{20}{h}$

RS-20. In the previous problem, the Giant **1** was drawn for you. As you solve the following proportions, draw your own Giant **1** if you find it helpful.

a) $\frac{1}{4} = \frac{2.5}{n}$

b) $\frac{3}{4} = \frac{36}{w}$

c) $\frac{7}{5} = \frac{x}{22.5}$

d) $\frac{3}{4} = \frac{n}{22}$

RS-21.   Copy the proportion $\frac{25}{45} = \frac{15}{27}$.

    a)   Reduce each ratio to confirm that the ratios are equal.

    b)   Multiply both sides of the original ratio by 27. You now have $27 \cdot \frac{25}{45}$ on the left side of the equation. What do you have on the right side?

    c)   Since you knew the original equation was true, how do you know the new equation is true?

    d)   Multiply both sides of the equation from part (b) by 45. On the left side of the equation you now have $27 \cdot 25$. What do you have on the right side?

    e)   Doing the two multiplications as above is known as cross multiplying. Why do you think it has this name?

    f)   How do you know that if you start with two equal ratios that you will always end up with two equal products after cross multiplying?

RS-22.   Now we want to cross multiply to confirm that some proportions are equal.

    a)   Verify that $\frac{3}{12} = \frac{5}{20}$ by cross multiplying.

    b)   Verify that $\frac{14}{49} = \frac{22}{77}$ by cross multiplying.

    c)   Suppose you know that $\frac{x}{3} = \frac{4}{6}$ is a true proportion. What true equation do you get without fractions by cross multiplying? Use this equation to find x.

RS-23. You have been using the Giant **1** to find equivalent fractions in a proportion. Some problems are easier to solve than others. For the problem $\frac{x}{30} = \frac{40}{100}$, you could not use a whole number in the Giant **1**. Instead, you can use cross multiplication to solve this proportion. The procedure is shown below for two proportions.

SOLVING PROPORTIONS WITH CROSS MULTIPLICATION

In a proportion, **CROSS MULTIPLICATION** is finding the product of the numerator (top) of one ratio and the denominator (bottom) of the other ratio, multiplying the other numerator and denominator together, and setting the products equal.

For any proportion $\frac{a}{b} = \frac{c}{d}$, after cross multiplication the result is $\mathbf{a \cdot d = b \cdot c}$.

Example: Use cross multiplication to solve for x in each proportion.

Step 1 Group any numerator and denominator elements together with parentheses if any part is a sum.

$$\frac{x}{30} = \frac{40}{100} \qquad \frac{(x+1)}{2} = \frac{3}{5}$$

Step 2 Cross multiply (multiply the numerator of each ratio by the denominator of the other ratio) to write an equation without fractions.

$$\frac{x}{30} \diagup\!\!\!\diagdown \frac{40}{100} \qquad \frac{(x+1)}{2} \diagup\!\!\!\diagdown \frac{3}{5}$$
$$x \cdot 100 = 30 \cdot 40 \qquad 5(x+1) = 2 \cdot 3$$

Step 3 Solve for x.

$$100x = 1200 \qquad 5x + 5 = 6$$
$$x = 12 \qquad 5x = 1$$
$$x = \tfrac{1}{5}$$

To the right of the double-lined box in your Tool Kit, write and solve the following problems using the cross multiplication method. Be sure to show all your steps. Check your answers with your partner or team to be sure they are correct.

a) $\frac{x}{10} = \frac{42}{12}$

b) $\frac{7}{n} = \frac{4}{36}$

c) $\frac{x+2}{5} = \frac{6}{10}$

RS-24.   An airplane travels 1900 miles in four hours.

a)   Find how far the airplane travels in one hour.
      Show all of your work.

b)   Use the information from part (a) to find
      how far the airplane travels in five hours.

RS-25.   Solve for x.

a) $\dfrac{x + 1}{2} = \dfrac{21}{7}$ b) $-4x + 31 = -3(x + 6)$ c) $-64 = -4x + 2x - 6x$

RS-26.   Simplify each expression by combining like terms.

a) $2x^2 + 5 - 13x + 11x - 2x^2 + 22$ b) $-12 + x - 5x^2 + 3x^3 - 10 + 4x - 2x^3$

c) $-2x^2 + 9 - 14x - (-9x^2) + 10 + 5x^2$ d) $2x^2 + (-x) + (-2x^2)(-1) + 13x - 6x^2$

RS-27.   Repeated multiplication of the same factor can be written with exponents. Rename
          each product using exponents. Example: $5 \cdot 5 \cdot 5 = 5^3$.

a) $2 \cdot 2 \cdot 2 \cdot 2 \cdot 2 \cdot 2$ b) $3 \cdot 3 \cdot 3 \cdot 3$

c) $2 \cdot 2 \cdot 2 \cdot 2 \cdot 2 \cdot 2 \cdot 2$ d) $6 \cdot 6 \cdot 6 \cdot 6 \cdot 6$

e) $4 \cdot 4 \cdot 4$ f) $x \cdot x$

RS-28.   A week of high and low temperatures in degrees
          Fahrenheit is shown at right. Make a double line graph
          to display these data. Remember to scale and label both
          axes.

Day	Low	High
Sun	43	82
Mon	50	101
Tues	53	105
Wed	45	90
Thur	44	91
Fri	43	88
Sat	45	90

RS-29.   Rename each exponential expression as a product without exponents.

a) 4^6 b) 7^4 c) 8^7

d) 9^5 e) 2^2 f) y^3

RS-30. Hannah and Breanna were working on a problem about exponents. The problem was: "Evaluate 2^3." Hannah wrote $2^3 = 2 \cdot 3 = 6$. Breanna wrote $2^3 = 2 \cdot 2 \cdot 2 = 8$. Who is correct? Explain why.

RS-31. Calculate the area of the rectangle at right.

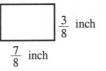

$\frac{3}{8}$ inch

$\frac{7}{8}$ inch

RS-32.

> ## PARALLELOGRAM VOCABULARY
>
> Two lines in a plane (flat surface) are **PARALLEL** if they never meet. The distance between the parallel lines is always the same. The marks >> indicate that the two lines are parallel.
>
> The **DISTANCE** between two parallel lines or segments is indicated by a line segment perpendicular to both parallel lines (or segments).
>
> A **HEIGHT** (h) is the <u>perpendicular</u> <u>distance</u>:
>
> - in triangles, from a vertex (corner) to the line containing the opposite side.
>
> - in quadrilaterals, between two parallel sides or the lines containing those sides.
>
> Any side of a two-dimensional figure may be used as a **BASE** (b).
>
> A **PARALLELOGRAM** is a quadrilateral (a four-sided figure) with both pairs of opposite sides parallel.

Highlight the following key words in your Tool Kit:

a)   "never meet," "distance between," and "same" (parallel);

b)   "perpendicular distance" and "line containing opposite side" (height, triangle);

c)   "between two parallel sides" (height, quadrilateral); and,

d)   "four-sided" and "opposite sides parallel" (parallelogram).

RS-33. Obtain the resource page from your teacher. Then carefully cut out the parallelogram.

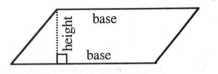

a) Label the bases and the height as shown.

b) Use a ruler to measure the base and height in centimeters. Label their lengths.

c) Cut along the height to separate the triangle from the rest of the figure. Then move the triangle to the other side of the figure, as shown at right. Paste, glue, or tape the pieces in your notebook.

d) What is the shape of the new figure?

e) If you were to cut the parallelogram along any other placement of the height, would you get the same figure? Try it with the second parallelogram. Explain in a complete sentence.

f) Find the area of the new rectangle.

RS-34. Discuss the difference between h and c in the figure at right. If A = area, use the variables shown to write a formula for calculating the area of the parallelogram.

RS-35. Tabitha's answer to the previous problem was $A = b \cdot h$. Midori's answer was $A = b \cdot c$. Which student was correct? Write a note to the student who had the incorrect answer, explaining how she can remember the correct way to calculate the area of a parallelogram.

RS-36. Percent is a ratio that compares a number to 100. Follow the model shown below and express each of the following ratios as a percent.

Example: $\frac{1}{5} = \underline{} \%$ $\Rightarrow$ $\frac{1}{5} = \frac{x}{100}$ $\Rightarrow$ $\frac{1}{5} = \frac{20}{100}$ $\Rightarrow$ 20%.

a) $\frac{1}{4}$ b) $\frac{3}{10}$

c) $\frac{17}{25}$ d) $\frac{9}{5}$

RS-37.

PERCENTAGES

To solve a percentage problem you can use a proportion. There are four quantities to consider in your proportion: the percent (i.e., <u>part</u> of 100), 100, the whole, and a part of the whole. One of these quantities will be unknown.

Example: What number is 25% of 160?

$$\frac{\%}{100} = \frac{part}{a\ whole}$$

- Set up your proportion with the percent numbers on one side and the quantities you wish to compare on the other side.

$$\frac{25}{100} = \frac{x}{160}$$

- Cross multiply to write an equation without fractions.

$$25 \cdot 160 = 100x$$

- Solve for the unknown.

$$x = 40$$

a) The cost for a hotel room for three nights was $188, including $14 tax. What percent of the bill was the tax? Complete parts (i) - (iv) to the right of the double-lined box in your Tool Kit.

  i) In this case, the whole is ...   ii) The part is ...

  iii) The proportion we need to solve is ...

  iv) What percent of the bill was the tax?

b) Ian got an 80% on his math test. If he answered 24 questions correctly, how many questions were on the test?

c) Ellen bought soccer shorts on sale for $6 off the original price of $40. What percent did she save?

RS-38. Find the area of the following figures.

a)

8 m

12 m

b)

8 m   14 m

12 m

c)

12 m

16 m

d)

9 m

2 m

RS-39.   Make a correlation statement for each scatter plot below.

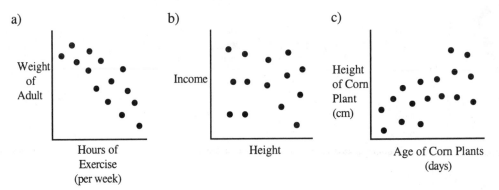

a) Weight of Adult / Hours of Exercise (per week)

b) Income / Height

c) Height of Corn Plant (cm) / Age of Corn Plants (days)

RS-40.   The simplified form of $\frac{8-6}{4} \cdot 2$ is:

(A) 2.5   (B) 1   (C) -2.5   (D) 2

RS-41.   Solve the following problems.

a) $3\frac{1}{2} + 2\frac{5}{8}$ b) $\frac{26}{11} + 7$ c) $5 - 1\frac{10}{13}$

RS-42.   Here is a set of data: 17, 24, 12, 4, 7, 22, 63, 14, 7. What is the outlier?

(A) 4   (B) 63   (C) 12   (D) 14

RS-43.   Express each of the following ratios as a percent. Refer to problem RS-36 if you need help

a) $\frac{1}{5}$ b) $\frac{19}{25}$ c) $\frac{19}{10}$ d) $\frac{3}{12}$

RS-44.   Solve each equation.

a) $\frac{2}{3} = \frac{6}{x+1}$ b) $13x - 5 = -x - 19$ c) $14x - 62 = -(-12x)$

RS-45.   Use $<$, $>$, or $=$ to compare the number pairs below.

a)   0.183 ___ 0.18   b)   -13 ___ -17

c)   0.125 ___ $\frac{1}{8}$ d)   -6 ___ -4

e)   72% ___ $\frac{35}{50}$ f) |-9| ___ 9

g)   -0.25 ___ -0.05   h)   -2.07 ___ -2.007

RS-46.   On your resource page find the
          parallelogram that looks like the one
          at right. Carefully cut it out.

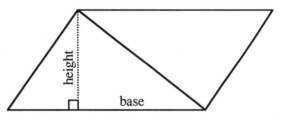

a)   Label the base and height.

b)   Use a ruler and measure the
      base and height in centimeters.
      Label them.

c)   Find the area of the parallelogram.

d)   Cut the parallelogram along the diagonal. What shapes did you make?

e)   Label the base and height on both triangles and glue, paste, or tape the triangles in
      your notebook. What is the area of each triangle?

f)   How does the area of each of the triangles compare to the area of the parallelogram?

RS-47.   A quadrilateral with one pair of parallel sides is called a trapezoid
          (see the picture at right for an example). Follow the steps below
          to develop a formula for finding the area of a trapezoid.

a)   The resource page given to you by your teacher has a pair of congruent trapezoids.
      Carefully cut them out.

b)   Measure the **bases** (the parallel sides) and the height of the trapezoid you cut out
      and record these measurements on your cut-out piece. Use centimeters.

c)   Rotate the second copy of the trapezoid and place it "end-to-end" with the first. If
      you have done this correctly, the figure should form a parallelogram.

d)   What are the base and height of this parallelogram?

e)   Find the area of the parallelogram.

f)   Using the area of the parallelogram you found in part (e), find the area of the
      trapezoid. What was your last step?

RS-48.   Christa saw that she could find the area of a trapezoid without cutting. She said that the base of the big parallelogram would be the sum of the two bases of the trapezoid.

   a)   Was she correct? Explain to your partner.

   b)   Then Christa said that she could write the area as a formula. If t is the length of the top base and b is the length of the bottom base, then the base of the big parallelogram is b + t and the area of the big parallelogram is (b + t) · h. Using the figure from the last problem, explain to the other members of your team why Christa's method to find the area of the parallelogram is correct.

   c)   Now that you know the area of the big parallelogram, what do you need to do to find the area of the original trapezoid?

RS-49.   Show how to use Christa's method to find the area of each of these trapezoids.

   a)   b)

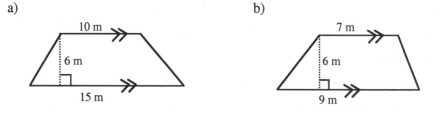

RS-50.   Ray decided to make some triangular corrals for Muggs the grumpy steer to improve his disposition. Ray will always start with a rectangle or parallelogram and fence off part of it to make the corrals. Find the area of each shaded, triangular corral.

RS-51.   Look at the areas you calculated in the previous problem.

a)   In each of the corrals, what fraction of the rectangle or parallelogram is the shaded triangle? (Calculate the areas of the rectangles or parallelograms, if you need to.)

b)   Earlier we concluded the area of a parallelogram is base · height. What can you conclude about calculating the area of a triangle?

RS-52.

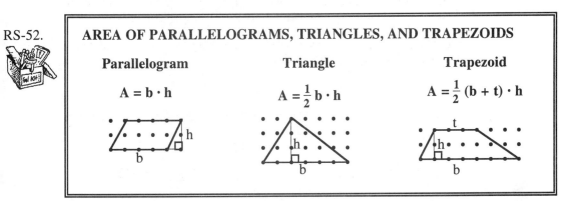

AREA OF PARALLELOGRAMS, TRIANGLES, AND TRAPEZOIDS

Parallelogram

$A = b \cdot h$

Triangle

$A = \frac{1}{2} b \cdot h$

Trapezoid

$A = \frac{1}{2} (b + t) \cdot h$

Write the following notes to the right of the double-lined box in your Tool Kit.

Calculate the area of each shape in the Tool Kit using the area formulas.

RS-53.   The height of a triangle is drawn from a vertex perpendicular to the line containing the opposite side. It is usually drawn using a dashed line.

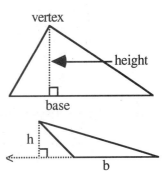

a)   Explain why the line should be dashed.

b)   Why is the small square drawn where the height meets the base?

c)   Explain why the height in the second triangle does not intersect the base.

RS-54.   The graph of the absolute value may surprise you. Complete the table below for the equation $y = |x| + 1$. Since $|-2| + 1 = 2 + 1 = 3$, one of the points will be (-2, 3).

x	-4	-3	-2	-1	0	1	2	3	4
y			3						

a)   Plot the points you calculated above to get the graph of $y = |x| + 1$.

b)   Describe the shape of the graph.

c)   Write the ordered pair for the point where the graph changes direction.

RS-55. For each circular object described, write the ratio $\frac{circumference}{diameter}$. Simplify each ratio.

    a) A circle with a diameter of 49 inches has a circumference of 154 inches.

    b) An embroidery hoop with a 14-inch diameter has a 44-inch circumference.

    c) A plate with a 22-inch circumference has a 7-inch diameter.

    d) Ray's watch face has a <u>radius</u> of 0.35 centimeters and a circumference of 2.2 centimeters.

    e) Compare the simplified ratios of $\frac{circumference}{diameter}$ from parts (a) through (d). What ⊂ you notice?

RS-56. Complete the following Diamond Problems.

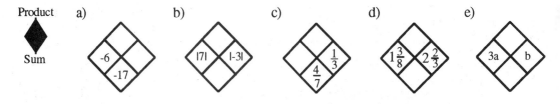

Product

Sum

    a)   b)   c)   d)   e)

RS-57. **Comparing the Circumference and Diameter of a Circle** For this investigati⊂ you will need a circular object and a flexible tape measure. Get these from your teache⊂

    a) Measure the diameter and circumference of your object to the nearest millimeter. the measurements your team provides to complete the first three columns of your

    b) Use the data from your table to write the ratio $\frac{circumference}{diameter}$ in the fourth column.

    c) Using a calculator, find the decimal approximations of the ratios $\frac{circumference}{diameter}$ to ⊂ nearest hundredth and enter your answers in the fifth column of the table.

    d) Examine the last two columns. What similarity do you notice in the ratio $\frac{circumference}{diameter}$ for the different size circles?

Name of Circular Item	Circumference (millimeters)	Diameter (millimeters)	Ratio of $\frac{circumference}{diameter}$	$\frac{circumference}{diameter}$ as a decimal
any circle				

RS-58.   You know the ratio $\frac{\text{circumference}}{\text{diameter}}$ is a little more than 3. If you know the diameter of a circle, how could you estimate the circumference?

RS-59.   For each of the circles drawn below, estimate the circumference.

a)   b)   c)   d)

RS-60.   Pi (π) is the name of the number that is the ratio $\frac{\text{circumference}}{\text{diameter}}$ for any circle. Because its value is not an exact integer or fraction, you must use an approximation when you calculate with it. There are several different approximations you can use for π depending on how accurate you need to be. Below we examine the effects of using some of these different approximations.

Suppose a circle has a diameter of 11 units.

a)   Calculate the circumference using the π button on a calculator. Round your answer to the nearest hundredth.

b)   Calculate the circumference using 3.14 for π. Round your answer to the nearest hundredth.

c)   Calculate the circumference using $\frac{22}{7}$ for π. Record your answer. Then convert your fraction to a decimal and round your answer to the nearest hundredth.

d)   Compare the answers to parts (a) through (c). Are the values fairly close or very different?

RS-61. Raj was watching his sister Balbir do her homework. Balbir drew three circles the same size. Balbir cut the first circle in four equal pieces. She cut the second circle into eight equal pieces. Balbir cut the third circle into sixteen equal pieces. Then Balbir pasted the circle pieces on her paper as shown below.

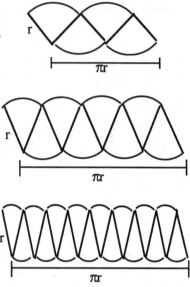

Raj: Why are you doing that, Balbir?

Balbir: I need to find a formula for the area of a circle. Each of these 'caterpillars' is helping me do that.

Raj: How?

Balbir: Look at the figures closely. As the number of pieces increases, you can see that they look more and more like a rectangle, right?

Raj: Yes, I see it. The area of a rectangle is base times height. What are the dimensions of these rectangles?

Balbir: The height of each rectangle is the radius of the circle, r. The length of the base of each rectangle is half the circumference so, it is πr.

Raj: That means that the area of the rectangle, base · height, is $\pi r \cdot r$, or πr^2.

Balbir: Since the area of the circle is exactly the same as the area of the rectangle, I'm finished!

a)   Use complete sentences to explain why the height of each rectangle is r.

b)   Use complete sentences to explain why the length of each rectangle is πr.

c)   Use complete sentences to explain why the area of the rectangle is $\pi r \cdot r$.

d)   Use complete sentences to explain why the area of the circle is πr^2.

RS-62. In a previous problem we learned that π is a number slightly larger than 3 which is not an exact integer or fraction. Since it cannot be written as the ratio of any two integers, it belongs to a special class of numbers known as **irrational** numbers. Whenever you want to be really accurate in your calculations, use the π button on your calculator which is accurate to about twelve decimal places. Modern computers have calculated π to more than four billion decimal places. Here are the first fifteen:

$$\pi \approx 3.141592653589793.$$

CIRCUMFERENCE OF CIRCLES

The **CIRCUMFERENCE** (C) of a circle is its perimeter, that is, the "distance around" the circle.

To find the circumference of a circle from its **diameter** (d), use $C = \pi \cdot d$.

To find the circumference of a circle from its **radius** (r), use $C = 2\pi \cdot r$.

Highlight "distance around the circle," "C = π · d," and "C = 2π · r" in your Tool Kit box.

RS-63.

AREA OF CIRCLES

To find the **AREA** (A) of a circle when given its radius (r), use the formula

$$A = \pi \cdot r \cdot r = \pi r^2$$

Write the following notes to the right of the double-lined box in your Tool Kit.

Using the area formula, calculate the area of a circle with a radius of 9.

RS-64. Calculate the circumference of the following circles, rounding each answer to the nearest tenth. All distances are in meters.

    a)   diameter = 10   b)   radius = 5   c)   diameter = 15   d)   radius = 10

RS-65. Calculate the area of the following circles, rounding each answer to the nearest tenth. All distances are in meters.

    a)   radius = 20   b)   diameter = 12   c)   radius = 3   d)   diameter = 15

RS-66. Compute.

a) $\frac{2}{6} + \frac{8}{14}$

b) $\frac{3}{5} \div \frac{6}{2}$

c) $\frac{53}{60} - \frac{7}{12}$

d) $\frac{3}{5} \cdot \frac{1}{5}$

RS-67. Susan can dig three post holes in 25 minutes. Use a proportion to determine how long it will take her to dig 14 post holes at the same rate. Round your answer to the nearest minute.

RS-68. An unknown number is decreased by seven, and the result is multiplied by three. The final result is 27. Find the unknown number.

a) Write an equation. A Guess and Check table might help you get started.

b) Solve for x algebraically. Show all of your steps.

RS-69. Jody found an $88 pair of sandals marked 20% off. What is the dollar value of the discount?

RS-70. Simplify each fraction by eliminating Giant **1**s.

a) $\frac{3 \cdot 4}{3 \cdot 6}$

b) $\frac{7 \cdot 2}{7 \cdot 4}$

c) $\frac{8 \cdot 9}{6 \cdot 8}$

d) $\frac{16 \cdot 4}{4 \cdot 8}$

e) Can any of your answers be simplified further by eliminating common factors? Check your answers.

RS-71. Solve these proportions using any method you choose. (You may use a calculator, but you m show all of your steps.)

a) $\frac{10}{y} = \frac{30}{100}$

b) $\frac{18}{15} = \frac{x}{100}$

c) $\frac{4}{7} = \frac{3x - 1}{35}$

RS-72. One method of looking at ratios is in relation to geometric shapes. Think of a copy machine and what it does to a picture when the "enlargement" button is selected. The machine makes *every length* of the picture larger by the same multiple. The angles of the enlarged figure have the same measures as the original figure. The picture below was enlarged by a factor of 3. We can also say it was enlarged by a ratio of 3 to 1. This can be written as $\frac{3}{1}$ because we are comparing the copy to the original and the sides of the copy are 3 times larger than those of the original.

Note: For all of these problems we will keep the original size dot paper in the enlargement (or reduction) so that you may compare the sizes of the figures.

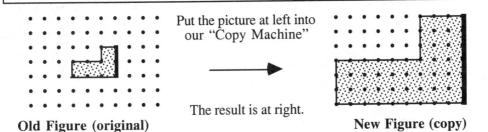

Put the picture at left into our "Copy Machine"

The result is at right.

Old Figure (original)　　　　　　　　　　　　**New Figure (copy)**

a) Your teacher will give you a resource page which has the original figure and the copy. These figures have six pairs of corresponding sides; one of the pairs has been darkened above.

b) Refer to the darkened pair of corresponding sides.

　i) What is the length of this side on the original figure?

　ii) What is the length of this side on the copy?

c) Write and simplify the ratio of this pair of sides in the order $\frac{copy}{original}$.

d) Choose another pair of corresponding sides in the figure. Write and simplify the ratio of these sides in the order $\frac{copy}{original}$.

e) Compare your simplified ratios from parts (c) and (d). What do you notice?

f) Predict the simplified ratio you would get for another pair of corresponding sides of the two figures. Now try it. Write and simplify the ratio for the remaining pairs of corresponding sides. Was your prediction correct?

RS-73.   Geometric figures can be reduced as well as enlarged. Think of the copy machine and
         what it does to a picture when you select the "reduction" button. The machine keeps the
         angles the same size and makes *every single length* of the picture equally smaller by the
         same multiple. Examine the figures below and note what resulted when the copy machine
         reduced the original figure. The copy machine produced a copy that has sides half the
         size of the original side lengths. We say this picture has been reduced by a ratio of 1 to 2
         or $\frac{1}{2}$. Again, we have not reduced the size of the dot grid.

Put the picture at left into our "Copy Machine"

(sides are multiplied by $\frac{1}{2}$)

The result is at right.

Old Figure (original)

New Figure (copy)

   a)   Locate at least three pairs of corresponding sides (there are eight in all), then write
        and simplify the ratio of each pair of corresponding sides in the order $\frac{copy}{original}$.

   b)   Compare the ratios. What do you notice?

RS-74.   Examine the figure at right.

   a)   Use dot paper to sketch the original figure. Label
        the dimensions.

   b)   Enlarge the figure by a ratio of $\frac{4}{1}$. Label the dimensions.

   c)   Write and simplify the ratio of one pair of corresponding sides in the order $\frac{copy}{original}$.

   d)   Calculate the perimeter of both the copy and the original. Write and simplify the
        ratio of the perimeters in the order $\frac{copy}{original}$.

SIMILARITY AND SCALE FACTORS

Two figures are **SIMILAR** if they have the same shape but not necessarily the same size. In similar figures:

- the corresponding angles have the same measures *and*
- the ratios of all corresponding pairs of sides are equal.

The simplified ratio of any pair of corresponding sides in similar figures is called the **SCALE FACTOR**.

Example for two similar triangles:

$$\frac{AB}{DE} = \frac{16}{40} = \frac{2}{5}$$

$$\frac{BC}{EF} = \frac{10}{25} = \frac{2}{5}$$

Write the following notes to the right of the double-lined box in your Tool Kit.

a) Write and simplify the ratio $\frac{AC}{DF}$.

b) What is the **scale factor** of similar figures (the ratio of their sides)?

RS-76. Patti claims she made a similar copy of each original figure shown in parts (a) and (b). For each pair of figures, write and simplify the ratios of each pair of corresponding sides in the order $\frac{copy}{original}$. Compare the ratios. Are the figures similar? (Did Patti really make a copy?) Assume that the corresponding angles are equal.

a) Original Figure   Copy   b) Original Figure   Copy

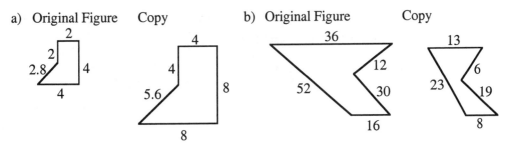

RS-77.   If two figures are similar, the ratio of corresponding sides will be equal. In the two simila
figures below, one side length is unknown. We write the proportion $\frac{5}{15} = \frac{x}{12}$. Solve for

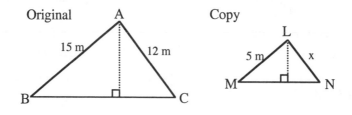

RS-78.   Identify the base and the height of each figure, then calculate the perimeter and area.

a)   b)

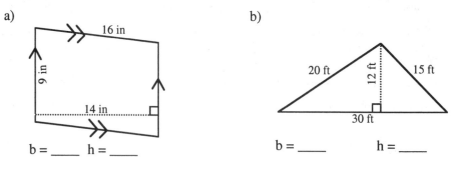

RS-79.   Solve for x.

a) $100 = 2(x + 4)$ b) $-2x + 11 = 5x + 39$ c) $-66 = -4x + 2x - 6$

ROTATION (TURN)

RS-80.   The dashed triangle ABC rotates 90°
counterclockwise about vertex A. Rotate
the dotted rectangle DEFG the same
way about vertex D. What are the
xy-coordinates of the corners of the
rectangle in its rotated position?

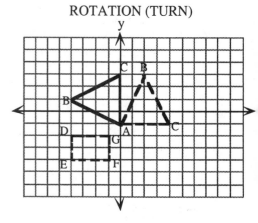

RS-81.   Ed went to dinner with some friends and decided to leave a good tip. The bill was $51.23

a)   If he left a 15% tip, how much did he pay in all?

b)   If Ed paid a total of $65, what percent tip did he leave?

CHAPTER 6

S-82.   Complete the following fraction-decimal-percent triangles.

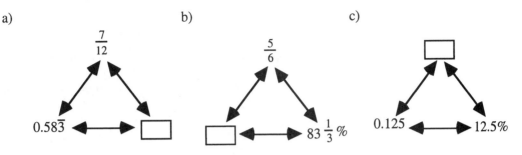

a)   b)   c)

$\frac{7}{12}$ $\frac{5}{6}$

0.58$\overline{3}$ ⟷ ☐   ☐ ⟷ 83$\frac{1}{3}$%   0.125 ⟷ 12.5%

S-83.   Mario asked Marisa for advice on this homework problem:
Rewrite $\frac{2^3}{2^4}$ without exponents, then simplify. Marisa said,
"Writing without exponents is the same as before. It's $2 \cdot 2 \cdot 2$
over $2 \cdot 2 \cdot 2 \cdot 2$." Mario said, "I see three Giant $\mathbf{1}$s in that
fraction, so it simplifies to 2. Wait! The 2 is in the denominator,
so it must be $\frac{1}{2}$." "Let's check. $\frac{2^3}{2^4}$ is $\frac{8}{16}$, and that simplifies to $\frac{1}{2}$,
so we're in good shape!" Rewrite the following expressions without exponents, then simplify.

a) $\frac{10^4}{10^1}$ b) $\frac{p^5}{p^2}$ c) $\frac{3^8}{3^4}$ d) $\frac{6^3}{6^3}$

S-84.   An example of using an exponent is $5 \cdot 5 = 5^2$. This problem is read as "five times five
equals five to the second power or five **squared**." When you use the exponent 2 you can
say you are "squaring" five because a square with a side of five has an area of $5 \cdot 5$,
which can be written as 5^2.

a)   Write "two squared" with and without exponents. Find its value.

b)   Write "three squared" with and without exponents. Find its value.

c)   Write "four squared" with and without exponents. Find its value.

d)   Write "ten squared" with and without exponents. Find its value.

RS-85.   Ray Sheo bought the plot of land shown at right
from his neighbor. Ray was not sure of all of
its dimensions, but he knew the two plots were
similar. Help Ray by completing parts (a) and
(b) below. Remember to write your ratios in the
order $\frac{new}{original}$.

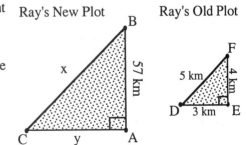

a)   The proportion $\frac{57}{4} = \frac{x}{5}$ is used to
calculate the length of x. Solve for x.

b)   Write and solve a proportion to calculate the length of y.

RS-86.   We have studied the ratio of corresponding sides of similar figures. Now we will look at the ratios of perimeters of similar figures. Use the template or block provided by your teacher. There should be a different-shaped template for each member of your team.

   a)   Trace your block. Label this as the original. Label each side as 1 or 2 units of length. What is the perimeter of your block? Write it near your figure.

   b)   Trace your block as many times as necessary to make a similar figure with a scale factor of $\frac{3}{1}$. Make sure your enlargement is exactly the same shape as the original with each side three times as long. Label this figure as the $\frac{3}{1}$ copy. Label the length of each side of the enlarged figure. Calculate the new perimeter.

   c)   Trace your block as many times as necessary to make a similar figure with a scale factor of $\frac{4}{1}$. Make sure your enlargement is exactly the same shape as the original with each side four times as long. Label this figure as the $\frac{4}{1}$ copy. Label the length of each side of the enlarged figure. Calculate the new perimeter.

   d)   For each enlargement, write and simplify the ratio of the perimeters in the order $\frac{cop}{origi}$

   e)   Compare your perimeter ratio with your team members who used a different shape.

   f)   Explain why you would expect the ratio of the perimeter to be the same as the scale factor.

RS-87.   Go back to the original figure you traced in the previous problem. In that problem we looked at ratios of perimeters. Now we will look at ratios of areas.

   a)   If the area of your original figure is one unit of area, how many units of area make up the figure with the scale factor of $\frac{3}{1}$? With the scale factor of $\frac{4}{1}$?

   b)   For each enlargement, write and simplify a ratio comparing the area of the enlarged figure to the original figure. Compare your results with those of your team members.

   c)   As a team, compare the answers from part (b) with the perimeter ratios for the figures. How are the area ratios and perimeter ratios related in terms of square numbers?

   d)   Area is measured in square units. Explain why it makes sense that the area ratios are the square of the perimeter ratios.

CHAPTER 6

RATIOS OF SIMILARITY

When figures are similar, the ratio of the perimeters is the same as the scale factor, $\frac{a}{b}$.

The ratio of the areas is the square of the scale factor, $\left(\frac{a}{b}\right)^2$.

The **PERIMETER RATIO** is $\left(\frac{\text{copy}}{\text{original}}\right)$ = scale factor = $\frac{a}{b}$.

The **AREA RATIO** is $\left(\frac{\text{copy}}{\text{original}}\right)$ = (scale factor)^2 = $\left(\frac{a}{b}\right)^2$.

For example, in the figures at right, the scale factor is $\frac{3}{1}$.

The perimeter ratio is $\frac{30}{10} = \frac{3}{1}$ = scale factor.

Perimeter = 10 m
Area = 6 m^2

Perimeter = 30 m
Area = 54 m^2

The area ratio is $\frac{54}{6} = \frac{9}{1} = \left(\frac{3}{1}\right)^2$ (the scale factor squared).

Highlight the ratios for perimeter and area in your Tool Kit.

RS-89.   Use the figures in problem RS-72.

a)   Calculate the perimeter and area for each of the figures.

b)   Write and simplify the ratio of the perimeters in the order $\frac{\text{copy}}{\text{original}}$.

c)   Compare the perimeter ratio to the scale factor. What do you notice?

d)   Write and simplify the ratio of the areas in the order $\frac{\text{copy}}{\text{original}}$.

e)   Compare the area ratio to the scale factor. Are these ratios the same? How is the area ratio related to the scale factor?

RS-90.   Two similar triangles have a scale factor of $\frac{5}{3}$.

a)   Find the perimeter ratio $\frac{\text{copy}}{\text{original}}$.   b)   Find the area ratio $\frac{\text{copy}}{\text{original}}$.

RS-91.   One triangle at right is a $\frac{5}{1}$ enlargement of another: $\frac{copy}{original} = \frac{5}{1}$.

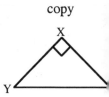

    a)   Find the perimeter of the original. (All measurements are in centimeters.)

    b)   Use a proportion to find the perimeter of the copy.

    c)   Use a proportion to find the area of the copy.

RS-92.   The two parallelograms at right are similar.

    a)   Find the missing length x.

    b)   Since neither height is given, you cannot calculate either area, but what is the <u>ratio</u> of the areas?

RS-93.   Use dot paper to sketch a copy of the original figure shown at right. Label the dimensions.

    a)   Enlarge the figure by a ratio of $\frac{3}{1}$. Label the dimensions.

    b)   Write the ratio of one pair of corresponding sides in the order $\frac{copy}{original}$.

    c)   Calculate the perimeter of the copy and the original. Write and simplify the ratio of the perimeters in the order $\frac{copy}{original}$.

    d)   Calculate the area of the copy and the original. Write and simplify the ratio of the areas in the order $\frac{copy}{original}$.

RS-94.   Solve for x.

    a) $\frac{5}{8} = \frac{4x + 3}{24}$ b) $10x + 15 = 2x - 9$ c) $14x - 13 = 1 + 12x$

RS-95.   Complete the following table and graph the rule: $y = -2x + 5$.

x	-1	0	1	2	3	4
y						

RS-96.   The following data set contains the ages of the people living near Ray Sheo's ranch:
44, 51, 11, 21, 61, 46, 11, 55, 94, 72, 56, 15, 86, 43, 11, 33, and 23.

a)   Organize the data in order from the smallest to the largest.

b)   What is the range?

c)   Find the mean, median, and mode.

d)   Draw a box-and-whisker plot of the data.

e)   Which measure of central tendency is most useful for Ray Sheo's nephew, Rob, who is in fifth grade and hoping to have friends to play with when he visits the ranch? Explain.

RS-97.   Tofu burgers are on sale at the local Super Duper Grocery Mart at 27.5% off. The same tofu burgers are also on sale at Better Buy Supermarket at $\frac{1}{4}$ off the regular price.

a)   If a package of tofu burgers usually costs $3.59 at either store, where should Marisa shop to get the best price?

b)   What price will she pay?

RS-98.   Follow your teacher's instructions for practicing mental math. Try a new strategy today. What did you choose?

RS-99. One of the following triangles is a reduction of the other. Write and solve proportions for each of the parts below.

a) Find the length of side MN.

b) Find the length of side ML.

c) Find the ratio of the areas of the two triangles.

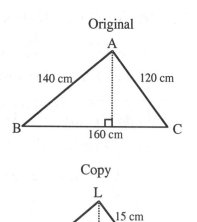

Original

Copy

RS-100. △ABC and △DEF are similar.

a) Find x.

b) Find y.

c) Find the ratio of the perimeters of the two triangles.

d) Find the ratio of the areas of the two triangles.

RS-101. Katie drew a parallelogram with a base of ten centimeters and a height of four centimeters. The other side of the parallelogram has a length of five centimeters.

a) Sketch the parallelogram that Katie drew. Label the dimensions.

b) Calculate the area and perimeter of Katie's parallelogram.

c) Katie's friend, Brooke, drew a parallelogram with every dimension three times larger. Calculate the area and perimeter of Brooke's parallelogram. Make a sketch of it if necessary.

CHAPTER 6

RS-102. The two triangles at right are similar.

a) Find x.

b) Find the area of the smaller triangle.

c) Based on ratios of similarity, use a proportion to find the area of the large triangle.

d) Find the area of the larger triangle by using the formula for the area of a triangle.

e) Verify that your answers to (c) and (d) are the same.

RS-103. A triangle is enlarged by a scale factor of $\frac{10}{3}$.

a) If the perimeter of the copy is 36 m, find the perimeter of the original triangle using the proportion $\frac{P_{copy}}{P_{original}} = \frac{10}{3}$.

b) If the area of the copied triangle is 48 m², use a proportion to find the area of the original triangle.

RS-104. Given two similar triangles, △ABC and △DEF, use proportions to find:

a) the perimeter of △DEF.

b) the area of △DEF.

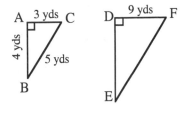

RS-105. Use ratios of similar figures to answer the following questions.

a) If you start with a 4-by-4 square and enlarge each side by a factor of $\frac{5}{4}$, calculate the perimeter and area.

b) Sketch the 4-by-4 square and its $\frac{5}{4}$ enlargement. Was your answer from part (a) correct? Explain in complete sentences.

c) Begin with a 6-by-9 rectangle and create a new smaller rectangle using a scale factor of $\frac{1}{3}$. Calculate the perimeter and area of the new rectangle.

d) Sketch a 3-by-5 rectangle and a $\frac{3}{1}$ enlargement of the rectangle. Calculate the perimeter and area of the enlargement.

RS-106. Identify the base and height, then find the perimeter and area of each figure below.

a)

15 yds   10 yds   12 yds

9 yds

b = _____   h = _____

b)

29 mm   24 mm

21 mm

b = _____   h = _____

RS-107. Solve the following equations for x. Check your solutions.

a) $6x + 13 = 3x - 5$

b) $2 + 3x = 14 + 7x$

c) $12 + 7x = 5(x + 2)$

d) $\frac{3}{5} = \frac{x + 8}{20}$

RS-108. Ray Sheo saw some socks on sale at the local department store. The advertised price was three pairs for $7.50.

a) How much would he pay for one pair?

b) How much would he pay for five pairs?

c) How much would he pay for seven pairs?

RS-109. Compute.

a) $\frac{4}{5} - \frac{2}{7}$

b) $\frac{18}{20} \cdot \frac{3}{2}$

c) $\frac{2}{3} + \frac{5}{8}$

d) $\frac{7}{9} \div \frac{3}{2}$

RS-110. Complete the following Diamond Problems.

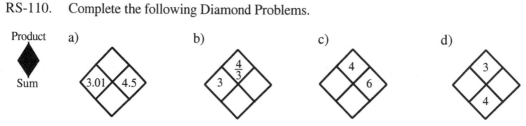

Product

Sum

a) 3.01   4.5

b) 3 $\frac{4}{3}$

c) 4   6

d) 3   4

S-111.   In the polygons at right, all
          corresponding angles are the same and
          the side lengths are as shown.

          a) Find the ratios of the
              corresponding sides.

          b) Are the two figures similar?

          c) What is the special name for similar
              figures with a scale factor of $\frac{1}{1}$?

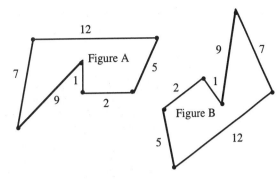

RS-112.   The scale factor of two similar figures is $\frac{5}{3}$. Write and solve a proportion to answer each of
          these questions.

          a)   If the perimeter of the smaller figure is 15 cm, what is the perimeter of the larger figure?

          b)   If the area of the larger figure is 50 cm², what is the area of the smaller figure?

RS-113.   A pair of similar triangles is shown at right.

          a)   Write and solve a proportion to find x.

          b)   Find the area of each triangle.

          c)   Write the ratio comparing the area of the
               small triangle to the area of the large triangle.

          d)   If you moved the smaller triangle on top of the larger
               triangle as shown at right, would that change the
               measurements or the ratios? Would it change the
               solution for x? Explain.

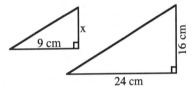

RS-114.   Examine the similar triangles at right. Decide if you want to
          compare the triangles as $\frac{\text{large}}{\text{small}}$ or as $\frac{\text{small}}{\text{large}}$.

          a)   Write and solve a proportion to find the missing leg of
               the smaller triangle.

          b)   Find the area of each triangle.

          c)   Write the ratio comparing the area of the small triangle to the area of the large triangle.

RS-115. Ray Sheo has a tall pine tree in his yard that is dying and needs to be cut down. Before he can cut it down, he needs to know how tall it is.

a) Ray decided to use what he knew about similar triangles to find the height of the tree. His first step was to stand so that the end of the shadow of the top of his head exactly matched the end of the shadow of the top of the tree. Then he measured the length of his shadow as 5 feet and the shadow of the entire tree as 65 feet. If you know that Ray is 6 feet tall, sketch and label a triangle diagram like the ones in the preceding problems. Use the information to label the parts of the diagram. Identify the two triangles.

b) Write a proportion and solve it to find the height of the tree.

RS-116. The biggest attraction at the new amusement park, World of Fun, is a huge slide that goes under the ground. To get to the top of the slide, Jon has to climb up a 56-foot ladder. Then he rides the slide to the bottom. Finally, Jon walks through a tunnel to the elevator and rides 35 feet to get back to ground level. The section of the slide that is above ground level is 77 feet long.

a) Use the similar triangles to find the length of the portion of the slide below ground level.

b) What is the total length of the slide?

RS-117. It is late in the day and Ray, who is 6 feet tall, casts a shadow that is 12 feet long. He is standing next to a flagpole that is 24 feet tall.

a) Sketch and label a diagram of this situation.

b) How long is the shadow of the flagpole? Explain your reasoning.

RS-118. Julia and her friend took the aluminum cans from the school recycling program and put them in five large paper bags. After school on Monday they took the cans to the recycling center and were paid a total of $12.50 for the five bags. On Tuesday they filled two more bags that were the same size as the others. How much should they expect to be paid for the two bags? Show all your work.

RS-119. Steve drives 65 miles per hour.

a) What is the ratio of miles to hours?

b) How many hours does it take for him to travel 130 miles from Portland to Tacoma?

c) How long will it take him to travel 390 miles?

d) How far can he travel in 4 hours?

e) How far can he travel in 8 hours?

RS-120. Name the four pairs of corresponding sides for these similar figures.

RS-121. Solve these proportions using cross multiplication. You may use a calculator, but you must show all your work.

a) $\dfrac{3 + x}{10} = \dfrac{4}{5}$

b) $\dfrac{2}{3} = \dfrac{4}{6 + x}$

c) $\dfrac{4 + x}{6} = \dfrac{3}{4}$

d) $\dfrac{8}{5} = \dfrac{2 - x}{7}$

RS-122. The problem "Simplify $\frac{2^4}{2^3}$" gave Mary and Katelyn some trouble.

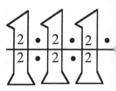

> *Mary:* The first part is easy. I'll write it without exponents. It's $\frac{2 \cdot 2 \cdot 2 \cdot 2}{2 \cdot 2 \cdot 2}$! But I'm stuck on the 'simplify' part.

> *Katelyn:* I see three Giant **1**s in that fraction, so it simplifies to 2.

a) Mary and Katelyn's work is shown above. Copy Mary's expanded fraction and draw Katelyn's Giant **1**s.

b) Simplify $\frac{2^4}{2^3}$ completely.

c) Use their example to simplify $\frac{3^6}{3^3}$.

RS-123. Jason was looking through his CD collection. When he sorted them by musical category, Jason found that he had 32 rock CDs, 27 classical, 18 jazz, 38 hip hop, 29 rap, 34 alternative, 78 oldies, 19 R & B, 24 gospel, and 11 country.

a) Make a stem-and-leaf plot of the CD data.

b) What is the mean number of CDs?

c) What is the median number of CDs?

d) What is the mode of the CDs?

RS-124. The original version of a textbook contained 1892 problems. The writers have decided to decrease the number of problems in the revised version by 23%. How many problems will they put in the revised book?

RS-125. These two similar triangles have a scale factor of $\frac{4}{3}$. Find the missing sides.

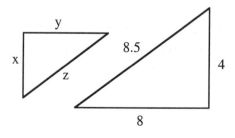

S-126.   Use the similar figures to complete each of the parts below.

a)   Side BC corresponds to side EF. To which
       side does side AB correspond?

b)   To which side does side DF correspond?

c)   Find the length of side DF.

S-127.   Ray Sheo, owner of the Pro-Portion Ranch,
             needs to build a bridge over the Roaring
             River that runs through his land. He has no
             idea how far it is across the river, but his
             daughter, Maria, knows she can find out by
             using the properties of similar triangles. Use
             the drawing at right and help Maria find the
             distance across the river.

In the diagram, the bridge is to go from D to
E. Maria began by walking from D in a
direction perpendicular to segment DE. After 6 feet she put a pole at point C and walked
another 8 feet to point B. Then she turned away from the river and walked in a direction
perpendicular to segment BD until she came to point A, which was 30 feet from point B.
From there she could see that A, C, and E were all in a straight line. Her result was two
similar triangles, ΔABC and ΔEDC.

a)   Sketch and label the figure on your paper. Be sure to include the measurements.
       Decide which parts of the two similar triangles correspond. You may want to re-
       draw the similar triangles so that they are facing the same direction.

b)   Write a proportion and find the distance across the river.

c)   The bridge will cost $1250 per linear foot. Calculate the complete cost of the bridge.

d)   Ray also needs to build an approach to the bridge on each side of the river. It costs
       $17.50 per hour to operate the tractor he will need to do the work. Each approach takes
       five hours of work. How much will it cost to use the tractor to complete the work?

e)   What is the total cost of the bridge?

S-128.   Ray and Carmen Sheo need a new driveway 50 feet long in front of their house. The old
             driveway is 30 feet long and cost $3000. Write a proportion using $\frac{\text{cost in dollars}}{\text{feet}}$ and solve
             it to determine the cost of the new driveway. Remember to label the units.

RS-129. Ray Sheo rented the Mightee Ditch Digger so he could dig a trench for a sprinkler line. He can dig a trench 300 feet long in 2 hours. Use a proportion to find out how long it w[ill] take him to dig a trench 850 feet long.

RS-130. Isabella wants to draw a copy of a suspension bridge for the cover of her book. She wants the proportions to be correct. The real bridge has two towers which are 746 feet high (from C to D). The main span is 4200 feet long (from A to B). Isabella wants the main span of her copy to measure 21 inches long.

a) How tall will Isabella's copy be?

b) The midpoint of the roadway (point E) is 265 feet above the water. How high above the "water" will Isabella's copy be?

RS-131. Frederico wants to build a new house identical in every way except size to the house where he grew up. He wants his new house to be 1.75 times as big.

a) If his childhood home measures 50 feet long by 30 feet wide, what are the dimensions of his new house?

b) If the square footage of Frederico's childhood home is 2250 square feet (some parts of the house are two stories), what is the square footage of his new home?

RS-132. Use the circles at right to solve these problems.

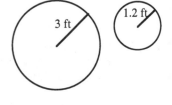

a) Find the circumference of each circle.

b) Find the ratio of circumferences, large to small.

c) Find the diameter of each circle.

d) Find the ratio of diameters, large to small.

e) Find the ratio of areas, large to small.

f) Are the relationships for ratios of similar polygons also true for circles? Explain.

RS-133. Calculate the perimeter and the area of each of the figures.

a)

b)

RS-134. Combine like terms. Show all steps.

a) $3(x^2 + x) - 4x + 12x^2 - 21x + 5$ b) $-2 - 4 + 2x^2 + 60x + 5x(10 + x)$

c) $-2(10 + x) - 4 - 2x^2 + x + 5x^2$ d) $2x^2 + 60x + (-2x)(-1) + 3x - 6$

RS-135. One day Sara, a fitness trainer, recorded the number of minutes her clients spent exercising so she could determine how long to make her classes.

42, 40, 52, 45, 55, 40, 61, 55, 50, 70, 67, 65, 37, 47, 34, 60, 59, 71, 36, 58, 33, 75, 77, 75, 35, 48

a) Use the data above to make a stem-and-leaf plot.

b) What is the range?

c) What is the mode of the data?

d) Which measure of central tendency provides the best information to help Sara plan the lengths of her classes? Explain.

RS-136. Steve has collected 45 key rings, 25 yo-yos, and 5 CDs to be given as prizes at the school math fair. He wants to design a spinner where the chances of winning each prize are about the same as the number of prizes he has. Help him design the spinner.

a) How many total prizes does he have?

b) Write the number of each prize as a fraction of the total. Simplify each fraction.

c) Use the simplified fractions from part (b) to design Steve's spinner.

RS-137.   Renata has a collection of 30 CDs, and she buys
           four new CDs each month. Her cabinet holds 150
           CDs. In how many months will Renata need a new
           cabinet for her CD collection?

           a)   Write a variable equation to represent the
                problem. A Guess and Check table might
                help you get started.

           b)   Solve the equation using algebra. Show all of
                your steps.

RS-138.   Mary was 4' 3" tall and weighed 85 pounds at the beginning of last year. Now she is 15%
           taller and 5% heavier. What are her height and weight now?

RS-139.   Follow your teacher's instructions for practicing mental math. Describe a method used
           by your partner or study team member.

RS-140.   **Chapter Summary** It is time to summarize and review
           what you have learned in this chapter. Your teacher will
           give you the format you will use.

RS-141.   Ray Sheo has two similarly shaped triangular plots of land. He needs to put some fencir
           around them. He knows the lengths of some of the sides, but he needs to know all the
           dimensions. Use the properties of similar triangles to find the unknown dimensions of
           the smaller plot of land.

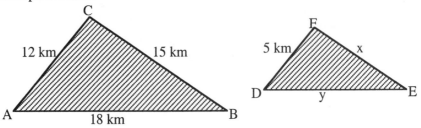

-142. Carmen Sheo is using a cake recipe that requires that the ratio of oil to water be $\frac{2}{3}$.
If she needs $\frac{1}{2}$ a cup of oil, how much water does she need?

-143. Ray's son, Martin, plays for a minor league baseball team, the Cow-a-bungas. He is the star player, an outfielder with a batting average of 0.340. (Batting average is the ratio of the number of times a player gets a hit to the number of times at bat.) If Martin was at bat 570 times during the season, how many hits did he get? Remember that batting average is based on the number of hits out of 1000.

-144. A school cafeteria's recipe for making the day's supply of bread requires 20 cups of water for every 50 cups of flour. Write and solve a proportion to find the amount of water needed if the amount of flour is 60 cups.

-145. Light travels 186,000 miles per second. On average, the light from the moon takes $1\frac{1}{4}$ seconds to reach Earth. How far away is the moon?

-146. Each ratio below compares the circumferences of an enlarged or reduced circle to the original. Simplify each ratio by using a Giant **1** to avoid using the π key. State whether the new circle is an enlargement or a reduction.

a) $\frac{6\pi}{3\pi}$ b) $\frac{44\pi}{66\pi}$ c) $\frac{44\pi}{11\pi}$ d) $\frac{6\pi}{24\pi}$

-147. Zelda photocopied a rectangle that was 10 centimeters by 16 centimeters. She set the enlargement feature to 125%. Write proportions and solve them to find the new dimensions.

-148. Solve these proportions using cross multiplication. You may use a calculator, but you must show all of your steps.

a) $\frac{35}{70} = \frac{x}{100}$ b) $\frac{12}{33} = \frac{m}{11}$ c) $\frac{x}{15} = \frac{12}{75}$

d) $\frac{4}{32} = \frac{10.5}{x}$ e) $\frac{12}{32} = \frac{x+5}{100}$ f) $\frac{8}{3} = \frac{50}{y-7}$

RS-149. Lorca said she saved $5, which was 30% of the original price of the CD she bought.

a) Set up a proportion that will allow you to find the original cost.

b) Solve the proportion and find the original cost of the CD.

RS-150. The members of the Calculator Club at another school called two t-shirt vendors in their town. One store charges a fee of $55 plus $3.75 per shirt. The second store charges a $75 fee plus $2.50 per shirt. What number of t-shirts makes the total cost the same?

a) Write an expression for the cost each company would charge for x t-shirts.

b) Set the expressions equal to each other and solve algebraically to answer the question

RS-151. Simplify each fraction by writing out all the factors first.

a) $\frac{42}{105}$

b) $\frac{27}{72}$

c) $\frac{35}{49}$

RS-152. Solve for x.

a) $2(x + 18) = 10$

b) $3(2x - 3) = -3$

c) $24 = 2(2x + 4)$

d) $3(2x - 1) = 9$

e) $4(2x + 1) = -28$

f) $2(x - 4) = x - 7$

g) $2(x + 8) = 3x - 3$

RS-153. **What We Have Done in This Chapter**

Below is a list of the Tool Kit entries from this chapter.

- RS-1   Congruent
- RS-3   A Ratio
- RS-6   Proportion
- RS-23   Solving Proportions with Cross Multiplication
- RS-32   Parallelogram Vocabulary
- RS-37   Percentages
- RS-52   Area of Parallelograms, Triangles, and Trapezoids
- RS-62   Circumference of Circles
- RS-63   Area of Circles
- RS-75   Similarity and Scale Factors
- RS-88   Ratios of Similarity

Review all the entries and read the notes you made in your Tool Kit. Make a list of any questions, terms, or notes you do not understand. Ask your partner or study team members for help. If anything is still unclear, ask your teacher.

The Class Tournament

Chapter 7

Chapter 7

The Class Tournament:
DIVISION OF FRACTIONS, PERCENTS, AND FORMULAS

In this chapter you will extend your equation solving skills. You will apply these skills in several new situations and use formulas to help you solve problems.

In this chapter you will have the opportunity to:

- divide fractions.

- find percentages, both of increase and decrease.

- use formulas to solve problems.

- solve literal equations.

- solve equations that have a fraction as the coefficient of x.

Read the problem below. The class tournament will be held at the end of the chapter. Your teacher will let you know how to prepare for it.

CT-0.　　It is time for the class mathematics tournament. You and your classmates will demonstrate the math proficiency you have been developing during the school year. Your assignment is to write math problems with their complete solutions and answer the math problems written by your classmates. The object of the tournament is to answer the problems correctly and earn as many points as you can for your team. Good luck!

Number Sense	
Algebra and Functions	
Mathematical Reasoning	
Measurement and Geometry	
Statistics, Data Analysis, & Probability	

Chapter 7
The Class Tournament:
DIVISION OF FRACTIONS, PERCENTS, AND FORMULAS

CT-1. Copy the rectangles in part (a). Partition them into the given fractional parts. The first one has been done for you. You do <u>not</u> need to draw figures for parts (b) through (d).

a)

thirds   fourths   fifths

b) If you draw a rectangle in which one-third of it is cut into 20 parts, how many parts are in the other two-thirds? How many parts is the whole rectangle cut into?

c) If one-fourth of a rectangle is cut into 25 parts, how many parts are in three-fourths? How many parts is the whole rectangle cut into?

d) If two-fifths of a rectangle is cut into 50 parts, how many parts are in three-fifths? How many parts is the whole rectangle cut into?

CT-2. Solve the following equations for x.

a) $8x = 96$ b) $5x = 225$ c) $9x = 120$

d) What operation did you use to solve each of these equations?

CT-3. The Poppington Poppers are sponsoring a tournament. After much research, Nishi found a perfect park in which to hold the tournament. He found that it would cost $60 to rent one-third of the park.

a) Draw a rectangle to represent the whole park. Divide this field into thirds (three equal parts).

b) How much does it cost to rent each part?

c) Suppose x represents the cost of renting the whole park. Write an equation that represents the situation.

d) How much would it cost to rent the whole park? Explain how you know.

CT-4.   Use the Three Way Table shown below to solve the following equations. Show three steps in your work: the fraction bar model, the equation for x from the model, and solving for x by division.

Fraction Bar	Equation for x from Model	Solving for x by Division

a) $\frac{1}{5}x = 95$ b) $\frac{1}{4}x = 56$

CT-5.   Jon painted $\frac{1}{4}$ of the snack bar in 2 hours. He wanted to find how long it would take hir to paint the whole snack bar.

a)   Represent the situation using a Three Way Table.

b)   How many hours does each part of the rectangle represent?

c)   How long would it take Jon to paint the whole snack bar?

CT-6.   Use a Three Way Table to solve the equation $\frac{2}{3}x = 70$. The picture at right represents this equation.

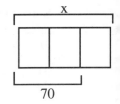

a)   Copy the fraction bar on your paper. If $\frac{2}{3}$ represents 70, what does $\frac{1}{3}$ represent? Explain how you know.

b)   What does x represent? Explain how you know.

CT-7.   Merci has driven 100 miles, which is $\frac{1}{5}$ of the way to Salt Lake City from her house. W is the total number of miles from her house to Salt Lake City? Use a Three Way Table t solve this problem.

CT-8.   Prepare your first card for the class tournament. Use the model provided by your teache

CT-9.   Use a Three Way Table to solve the equations in parts (a) through (d). Show your work

a) $\frac{1}{3}x = 65$ b) $\frac{1}{2}x = 43$

c) $\frac{1}{5}x = 75$ d) $\frac{1}{8}x = 25$

CT-10.   What is the mean of 4, 8, 2, 6, 3, 4, 4, 5, and 9?

(A) 8   (B) 6   (C) 5   (D) 4

CT-11.   The stem-and-leaf plot at right shows heights
          of corn plants, measured in centimeters, after
          a month of growth.

          a)   Find the median.

          b)   Another corn plant's height is slightly
                greater than the median and is added to
                the plot. Without calculating, select the
                best result for each of the three
                problems below.

```
 0 | 6
 1 | 2
 2 |
 3 | 8
 4 | 5 9
 5 | 3 6 8 9 9
 6 | 0 2 5 6
 7 | 3 6 9
 8 | 0 2 9
 9 | 8 8 8 9
10 | 2 5
```

Key
1 | 2 means 12

          i)   The median will: (A) Increase   (B) Decrease   (C) Stay the same

          ii)   The mode will: (A) Increase   (B) Decrease   (C) Stay the same

          iii) The range will: (A) Increase   (B) Decrease   (C) Stay the same

CT-12.   Solve for x. The variable y will be part of your answer.

          a) $10 + x = y$ b) $2x = 18 + 2y$ c) $2x - y = 8$

CT-13.   Compute: $\dfrac{4^2 + 8}{3} - 3$

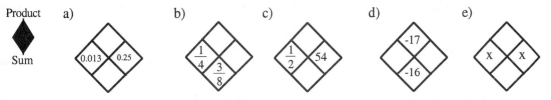

(A) -3   (B) 1   (C) -7   (D) 5   (E) none of these

CT-14.   Complete the following Diamond Problems.

Product

Sum

a)   b)   c)   d)   e)

The Class Tournament: Division of Fractions, Percents, and Formulas   253

CT-15.   Mae and Joe baby-sit to earn spending money. Mae charges $20 for the evening and three dollars for every hour she baby-sits. Joe charges no flat rate, but his hourly fee is seven dollars an hour.

   a)   Write an expression for the cost of an evening of baby-sitting by Mae.

   b)   Write an expression for the cost of an evening of baby-sitting by Joe.

   c)   Set the expressions in part (a) equal to each other to find out after how many hours they would make the same amount of money.

   d)   If you were to choose a baby-sitter based on how much Mae and Joe charge, who would you choose and why?

CT-16.   Now that we have started a new chapter, it is time for you to organize your binder.

   a)   Put the work from the last chapter in order and keep it in a separate folder.

   b)   When this is completed, write, "I have organized my binder."

CT-17.   Study the following division problems and the diagrams that represent them. Answer the question below each diagram.

   a) $8 \div \frac{1}{2}$

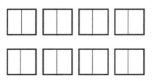

   How many halves?

   b) $8 \div \frac{1}{3}$

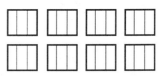

   How many thirds?

   c) $8 \div \frac{1}{4}$

   How many fourths?

   d) $8 \div \frac{1}{5}$

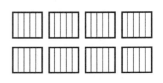

   How many fifths?

>>Problem continues on the next page.>>

e) $8 \div \frac{1}{6}$

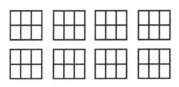

How many sixths?

f)   Use the idea from parts (a) through (e) to compute $8 \div \frac{1}{8}$ without drawing a picture. Explain how you get your answer.

CT-18.   Use your results from the preceding problem to write a multiplication problem that solves each division problem.

a) $24 \div \frac{1}{4}$ b) $8 \div \frac{1}{10}$ c) $12 \div \frac{1}{7}$

CT-19.   Set up a Three Way Table to solve the following equations. Show your work in each part. Below is an example that shows the steps involved in solving $\frac{1}{4}x = 18$.

Three Way Table

Fraction Bar Model	Equation for x from Model	Solving for x by Division
x, $\frac{1}{4}$, 18, 18	$x = 18 \cdot 4$ $x = 72$	$\dfrac{\frac{1}{4}x}{\frac{1}{4}} = \dfrac{18}{\frac{1}{4}}$ $x = 18 \div \frac{1}{4}$ $x = 72$

a) $\frac{1}{3}x = 24$ b) $\frac{1}{8}x = 12$ c) $\frac{1}{7}x = 10$

CT-20.   Multiply.

a) $\frac{1}{8} \cdot \frac{8}{1}$ b) $\frac{3}{4} \cdot \frac{4}{3}$

c) $\frac{2}{3} \cdot \frac{3}{2}$ d) $\frac{7}{1} \cdot \frac{1}{7}$

e)   The pairs of fractions in parts (a) through (d) are called **reciprocals**. Write three other pairs of reciprocals.

CT-21.   Replace each x with the number that makes the sentence true. For part (d), rewrite the mixed number as a fraction greater than one before you find the correct value for x.

a) $\frac{1}{4} \cdot x = 1$ b) $\frac{1}{5} \cdot x = 1$

c) $x \cdot \frac{3}{8} = 1$ d) $x \cdot 2\frac{1}{4} = 1$

e)   What is the result when a number is multiplied by its reciprocal?

CT-22.

RECIPROCAL or MULTIPLICATIVE INVERSE
Two numbers with a product of 1 are called **RECIPROCALS** or **MULTIPLICATIVE INVERSES**.
Examples: The reciprocal of 3 is $\frac{1}{3}$; of $\frac{2}{5}$ is $\frac{5}{2}$; of $\frac{1}{7}$ is 7.

Make these notes in your Tool Kit to the right of the double-lined box.

Why do you think the reciprocal is called the <u>multiplicative</u> inverse?

CT-23.   Write the number shown and its reciprocal (multiplicative inverse).

a) $\frac{1}{5}$ b) $\frac{2}{3}$ c)   7

d) $\frac{4}{5}$ e) $1\frac{2}{3}$ f) $3\frac{1}{4}$

g)   1.5   h)   0.25   i) $\frac{x^2}{y}$

CT-24.   Multiply each number and its reciprocal in the previous problem to verify that these numbers truly are reciprocals.

CT-25.   Solve the following problems.

a) $0.93 - \frac{3}{8}$ b) $\frac{6}{10} + 3.8$ c) $6\frac{3}{5} - 3.6$

CT-26. John has two six-sided dice. One is white; the other is green.

a) How many different ways are there for the two dice to land?

b) Make a complete outcome grid showing all the outcomes of rolling two dice. (Save this outcome grid in your notebook to use in future problems.)

Number on Green Die

		1	2	3	4	5	6
	1	1, 1	1, 2	1, 3	1, 4	1, 5	1, 6
Number	2	2, 1	2, 2	2, 3			
on	3	3, 1	3, 2				
White	4	4, 1					
Die	5						
	6						

CT-27. Miranda called her favorite radio station to play the game "Yes or No and Why." Here is her question: "If Ray has a square plot of land that has an area of 100 square feet and all the sides are doubled, is the area also doubled? In other words, is the area now 200 square feet?"

a) How should Miranda answer, yes or no?

b) Sketch a diagram to prove your answer and explain why it supports the answer you gave in part (a).

CT-28. Solve the following equations for x. Show your work.

a) $2x - 3 = 5$

b) $3x + 1 = 8.5$

c) $6 = 6x - 1.2$

CT-29. Solve the following equations. Show your work.

a) $\dfrac{x}{4} = \dfrac{12}{16}$

b) $\dfrac{y}{12} = \dfrac{12}{144}$

c) $\dfrac{7}{n} = \dfrac{3.5}{100}$

CT-30. Evaluate and compare. Use >, <, or =.

a) $-9 + 4$ ___ $5 - 7$

b) $|-5 + 2|$ ___ $|6 - 3|$

c) $14 - (-8)$ ___ $2 + -18$

d) $-7(-8)(-3)$ ___ $|-7(-8)(-3)|$

CT-31.   Prepare another card for the class tournament. Use the format given earlier.

CT-32.   Use the given diagrams to find x in parts (a) and (b).

a) $x = \frac{1}{2} \div \frac{1}{4}$

x indicates how many fourths there are in one-half.

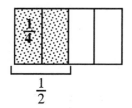

$\frac{1}{2}$

b) $x = \frac{3}{2} \div \frac{1}{4}$

x tells us how many fourths there are in three-halves.

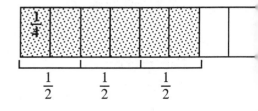

$\frac{1}{2}$ $\frac{1}{2}$ $\frac{1}{2}$

c)   Is $\frac{1}{2} \div \frac{1}{4}$ equivalent to $\frac{1}{2} \cdot \frac{4}{1}$? Explain why your answer makes sense.

d)   Is $\frac{\frac{1}{2}}{\frac{1}{4}}$ equivalent to $\frac{1}{2} \div \frac{1}{4}$? Why?

e)   Is $\frac{3}{2} \div \frac{1}{4}$ equivalent to $\frac{3}{2} \cdot \frac{4}{1}$? Why?

f)   Is $\frac{\frac{3}{2}}{\frac{1}{4}}$ equivalent to $\frac{3}{2} \div \frac{1}{4}$? Why?

CT-33.   Consider the steps shown below to solve the problem $\frac{1}{2}x = \frac{1}{3}$. Explain the mathematical process being done in each step.

Step 1 $\dfrac{\frac{1}{2}x}{\frac{1}{2}} = \dfrac{\frac{1}{3}}{\frac{1}{2}}$

Step 2 $x = \frac{1}{3} \div \frac{1}{2}$

Step 3 $x = \frac{1}{3} \cdot \frac{2}{1}$

Step 4 $x = \frac{2}{3}$

CHAPTER 7

CT-34. Use the model in the previous problem to solve $\frac{1}{4}x = \frac{3}{4}$.

CT-35. Is there another way to solve the equation in problem CT-33? Demonstrate it.

CT-36. Riley and Tara are discussing how to simplify this expression: $\frac{1}{2} \div \frac{3}{4}$.

Riley's Solution:

$$\frac{1}{2} \div \frac{3}{4} \quad\Rightarrow\quad \frac{1}{2} \cdot \frac{4}{3} \quad\Rightarrow\quad \frac{4}{6} \quad\Rightarrow\quad \frac{2}{3}$$

Tara's Solution:

$$\frac{1}{2} \div \frac{3}{4} \quad\Rightarrow\quad \frac{\frac{1}{2}}{\frac{3}{4}} \quad\Rightarrow\quad \frac{\frac{1}{2}\cdot\frac{4}{3}}{\frac{3}{4}\cdot\frac{4}{3}} \quad\Rightarrow\quad \frac{\frac{4}{6}}{\frac{12}{12}} \quad\Rightarrow\quad \frac{\frac{4}{6}}{1} \quad\Rightarrow\quad \frac{2}{3}$$

a) Explain what Riley did to solve the equation.

b) Explain what Tara did to solve the equation.

c) Compare the two solutions above. How are they different?

CT-37. Solve the following problems using either Riley's or Tara's method. Show your work.

a) $\frac{2}{3} \div \frac{2}{5}$

b) $\frac{9}{7} \div \frac{3}{4}$

CT-38. Angela does not understand how to solve $\frac{2}{7}x = 12$. Jared claims that he found an easy way to solve this problem without even drawing pictures. He says, "All we have to do is multiply both sides of the equation by 7, because $7 \cdot \frac{2}{7}x$ is 2x, and $7 \cdot 12 = 84$, so the equation becomes 2x = 84, which is simple to solve: x = 42.

a) Copy Angela's equation and discuss with your partner why Jared's method works.

b) Use Jared's method to solve $\frac{3}{4}x = 18$.

CT-39. Use Jared's method to solve the following equations. Show all steps.

a) $\frac{2}{3}x = 11$

b) $\frac{3}{4}x = 102$

c) $\frac{3}{10}x = 3.4$

d) $\frac{5}{8}x = \frac{1}{6}$

CT-40.   Sarah started doing part (d) of the previous problem using Tara's method. However, she quickly got stuck. She wrote:

$$\frac{\frac{5}{8}x}{\frac{5}{8}} = \frac{\frac{1}{6}}{\frac{5}{8}}$$

$$x = \frac{1}{6} \div \frac{5}{8}$$

"What do I do now? I don't know how to divide a fraction by a fraction," she moaned. Jared saw what she had done and thought she could still complete the problem. He told Sarah, "Every time we could divide to solve our equation we could also multiply to solve them. Can't we just rewrite the division as a multiplication problem using the reciprocal?"

Copy Sarah's work and complete it by rewriting the last step as multiplication using the reciprocal.

CT-41.

SOLVING EQUATIONS WITH FRACTIONAL COEFFICIENTS

Once an equation has been simplified so that the variable is isolated with a fractional coefficient, divide both sides by the fractional coefficient or multiply both sides by its reciprocal.

Example 1: $\frac{1}{4}x = 12$ Example 2: $\frac{3}{4}x = 12$

Solution A: Solution B: Solution A: Solution B:

$$\frac{\frac{1}{4}x}{\frac{1}{4}} = \frac{12}{\frac{1}{4}}$$

$$x = 12 \div \frac{1}{4}$$

$$x = \frac{12}{1} \cdot \frac{4}{1}$$

$$x = 48$$

$$\frac{1}{4}x = 12$$

$$\frac{4}{1} \cdot \frac{1}{4}x = 12 \cdot \frac{4}{1}$$

$$x = \frac{48}{1}$$

$$x = 48$$

$$\frac{\frac{3}{4}x}{\frac{3}{4}} = \frac{12}{\frac{3}{4}}$$

$$x = 12 \div \frac{3}{4}$$

$$x = \frac{12}{1} \cdot \frac{4}{3}$$

$$x = \frac{48}{3} = \frac{16}{1}$$

$$x = 16$$

$$\frac{3}{4}x = 12$$

$$\frac{4}{3} \cdot \frac{3}{4}x = 12 \cdot \frac{4}{3}$$

$$x = \frac{48}{3} = \frac{16}{1}$$

$$x = 16$$

Make these notes in your Tool Kit to the right of the double-lined box.

a)   Which solution method do you prefer? Why?

b)   How are the methods the same?

CT-42. Solve the following equations. Put one of these examples in your Tool Kit.

a) $\frac{1}{4}x = \frac{1}{8}$

b) $\frac{1}{9}x = \frac{1}{3}$

c) $\frac{2}{3}x = \frac{5}{6}$

CT-43. Solve for x. Show your work.

a) $x = \frac{1}{2} \div \frac{1}{4}$

b) $x = 3 \div \frac{1}{3}$

c) $\frac{2}{3} \div \frac{5}{6} = x$

d) $3x - 24 = -15$

e) $6 = 6x - 18$

f) $4x - 7 = x + 5$

g) $2(x + 8) = -34$

CT-44. Travis rolls his socks together in pairs and keeps them in his drawer. He has four pairs of black socks, six pairs of white socks, one pair of blue socks, one pair of gray socks, and three pairs of brown socks. Because of a power outage, he must take a pair out of the drawer in the dark. What are his chances of getting a pair of brown socks? Express your answer as both a fraction and a percent. Show your work.

CT-45. Solve the following equations. Remember to distribute first.

a) $21 = (x + 3)2$

b) $3(2x - 2) = 2$

c) $4x - 5 = 4(2x - 3)$

d) $-2(x + 4) = 5(x - 1)$

CT-46. Complete the following Diamond Problems.

Product

Sum

a)

b)

c)

d)

CT-47. Prepare another card for the class tournament.

CT-48.

DIVISION OF FRACTIONS

To divide fractions, multiply by the reciprocal of the divisor.

Example 1: $\frac{7}{6} \div \frac{2}{3} = \frac{7}{6} \cdot \frac{3}{2} = \frac{21}{12}$ or $\frac{7}{4}$

Example 2: $\dfrac{\frac{2}{3}}{\frac{5}{6}} = \frac{2}{3} \cdot \frac{6}{5} = \frac{12}{15}$ or $\frac{4}{5}$

Make these notes in your Tool Kit to the right of the double-lined box.

a)   Highlight the divisor in each of the examples.

b)   Rewrite example 2 as a division problem with a division sign ($\div$).

CT-49.

Write an equation or use a Guess and Check table to solve the following problem.

During one season, two apple trees and three pear trees produced a total of 126 pieces of fruit. Each apple tree produced the same number of apples, and each pear tree produced two more pieces of fruit than either apple tree. How many apples did each of Ray's apple trees produce in one season? Complete the table below and answer in a complete sentence.

CT-50.   Jon has $1500 in a special savings account that is earning interest at the **simple interest rate** of 3%. Jon will get 3% of $1500 ($0.03 \cdot \$1500 = \$45$) in interest this year. At the end of the year, he will have $1545. Sometimes people are paid simple interest for more than one year. If Jon earned 3% simple interest for 5 years, he would have earned $\$45 \cdot 5 = \$225$ in interest in that time.

The formula for the amount of money Jon would have after t years is $45t. In general, the formula is

$$A = P + I = P(1 + rt)$$

where:
- A stands for the amount of money at the end of t years.
- P stands for the principal, the amount of money Jon has now (P = $1500).
- I stands for the interest earned.
- r stands for the interest rate (r = 3% or 0.03).
- t stands for the time in years that the money has been in the account (t = 2 years).

a)   Use the formula to calculate how much money Jon will have after 2 years.

b)   Use the formula to calculate how much money Jon will have after 6 years.

CT-51.   Annie's goal is to have $2500 saved after two years. She has $2350 in the bank today. The bank will pay 3% simple interest on the money for two years. Will Annie reach her goal? Explain.

CT-52.   Samantha is twelve years old and has inherited $8000 from her grandfather to pay for college in six years. Her bank pays 5% **compound interest**. That is, the bank pays interest not only on the original principal, but also on the interest already earned.

a)   Complete the table to find out how much money Samantha will have at the end of each year.

Time (years)	Amount at Beginning of Year	Interest Paid	Amount at End of Year	Year-End Amount in Terms of Yearly Beginning Balance	Year-End Amount in Terms of Principal
1	$8000	$400	$8400	$8000 \cdot (1.05)$	$8000 \cdot (1.05)$
2	8400	420	8820	$8400 \cdot (1.05)$	$8000 \cdot (1.05)^2$
3				1.05)	$8000 \cdot (1.05)^3$
4				(1.05)	$8000 \cdot (1.05)^4$

b)   Where does the 1.05 come from?

c)   Use the pattern you see in the far right column to figure out how much money Samantha will have in 5 years. Then figure out how much money she will have in 6 years.

d)   Samantha's younger sister Tabitha got $5000 from her grandfather. She decides to put her money into a bank that pays 6% compound interest for 10 years. Write the formula to compute the total amount of money she will have after 10 years and use your calculator to find it.

CT-53.   From the previous problem, you know that the amount of money you have in a savings account that uses compound interest will be more than the amount of money you have in account that uses simple interest. The formula for computing the amount of money in a account with compound interest is

$$A = P(1 + r)^t$$

where:
- A stands for the amount of money at the end of t years.
- P stands for the principal, the amount of money Samantha has now (P = $8000).
- r stands for the interest rate (r = 5% or 0.05).
- t stands for the time in years the money has been in the account (t = 6 years).

a)   Use the formula to calculate how much money Samantha will have after 3 years. Compare this with your answer from CT-52.

b)   Use the formula to calculate how much money Samantha will have after 5 years.

CT-54.   Mary wants to have $8500 for a car when she is 21. She has $6439 in a savings account earning 4% compound interest. Mary is 13 now.

a)   Use the formula to find out how much money Mary will have when she is 15. Use t = 2.

b)   How much money will Mary have when she is 17? Use t = 4.

c)   Will Mary have enough money for the car when she is 21? Use t = 8.

CT-55.   Randy and Rita are twins who are planning to enter college in five years. They have $2000 to put in a savings account. They can invest the money at 4.5% simple interest or at 4.3% compound interest. Which interest rate should they choose? Show your work t support your answer.

CT-56.   Randy and Rita's baby sister, Rachel, has been given $1000 to put into a savings account. Her parents have to decide whether to put the money in a bank that pays 6% simple interest or 5% interest compounded annually. Use the information on your resource page to graph the amount of money that Rachel would have in her account over the next 15 years until she leaves for college.

CT-57.

┌───┐
║   SIMPLE INTEREST   ║
║   ║
║ **SIMPLE INTEREST** is interest paid only on the original amount of the principal ║
║ at each specified interval (such as annually). The formula is I = Prt, where   ║
║ I = Interest, P = Principal, r = rate, and t = time.   ║
║   ║
║ Example: Teresa invested $1425.00 (principal) in a savings account at her local ║
║   bank. The bank pays a simple interest of 3.5% annually (rate). How   ║
║   much money will Teresa have after 4 years (time)?   ║
║   ║
║   I = Prt   ⇒   I = (1425)(0.035)(4) = $199.50   ║
║   ║
║   ⇒   P + I = $1425 + $199.50 = $1624.50   ║
║   ║
║   Teresa will have $1624.50 after 4 years.   ║
└───┘

Make these notes in your Tool Kit to the right of the double-lined box.

a)   How would you find how much money Teresa would have after 10 years?

b)   In the Tool Kit box containing the formula I = Prt, highlight the line that includes what each variable represents.

CT-58.

┌───┐
║   COMPOUND INTEREST   ║
║   ║
║ **COMPOUND INTEREST** is interest paid on both the original principal and the   ║
║ interest earned previously.   ║
║   ║
║ The formula for compound interest is $A = P(1 + r)^t$, where A = total amount   ║
║ including previous interest earned, P = principal, r = interest rate, and t = time. ║
║   ║
║ Example: Teresa found another bank that paid 3.5% (rate) compounded annually.   ║
║   If she invests $1425.00 (principal), how much money will she have   ║
║   after four years (time)?   ║
║   ║
║ $A = P(1 + r)^t$ ⇒ $A = 1425(1 + 0.035)^4$ ║
║   ⇒ $1425(1.035)^4 = 1425 \cdot 1.1475 = \$1635.22$ ║
║   ║
║   Teresa will have $1635.22 after 4 years.   ║
└───┘

Make these notes in your Tool Kit to the right of the double-lined box.

Should Teresa have her interest compounded annually or should she receive simple interest? Why?

CT-59.   Judd was curious. He asked, "How would you solve the equation: $\frac{1}{6}x = \frac{1}{2}$?"
          Show him how to solve for x and state its value.

CT-60.   Solve the following equations for x.

          a) $\frac{1}{16}x = \frac{1}{4}$ b) $\frac{1}{3}x = \frac{1}{4}$

CT-61.   Consider Renzi's method for solving the following problem. Explain what he has done
          in each step to get his solution.

          Step 1 $\frac{5}{8} + 2\frac{3}{4}$

          Step 2 $\frac{5}{8} + \frac{11}{4}$

          Step 3 $\frac{11}{4} \cdot \frac{2}{2} = \frac{22}{8}$

          Step 4 $\frac{5}{8} + \frac{22}{8} = \frac{27}{8}$

          Step 5 $3\frac{3}{8}$

CT-62.   Follow the steps Renzi used to add the numbers in each problem.

          a) $3\frac{3}{5} + \frac{7}{10}$ b) $\frac{2}{3} + 4\frac{4}{9}$ c) $\frac{2}{5} + 1\frac{3}{4}$

CT-63.   Stacy and Noel are discussing whether or not Renzi's method would work with
          subtraction problems. Try these to find out.

          a) $2\frac{1}{8} - \frac{1}{4}$ b) $4\frac{3}{10} - 1\frac{1}{5}$

CT-64.   Alisa was riding her bike home from the baseball
          field. She wondered how long it would take her to
          get to her house. She noticed she was $\frac{2}{3}$ of the way

          home after $\frac{1}{2}$ an hour.

          a)   Write an equation to represent Alisa's problem.

          b)   What is the reciprocal of $\frac{2}{3}$?

          c)   Show that $\frac{2}{3}$ and $\frac{3}{2}$ are reciprocals. Use your Tool Kit entry for help.

          d)   Solve Alisa's equation. How long will it take her to get home?

CT-65.   Prepare another card for the class tournament.

CT-66.   Complete the following fraction-decimal-percent triangles.

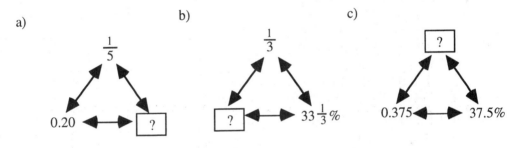

          a)   b)   c)

CT-67.   Solve each proportion for x. Show all your steps.

          a) $\frac{3}{4} = \frac{84}{x-3}$ b) $\frac{x}{7} = \frac{3}{5}$

          c) $\frac{x}{100} = \frac{5}{8}$ d) $\frac{21}{100} = \frac{x}{15}$

CT-68.   Erika, the head of the Booster Club, thinks the club can make money by selling shirts.
          She can buy a shirt for $6.00.

          a)   Erika wants to mark up (increase) the price by 50%. How much would a shirt cost
                with a 50% increase?

          b)   The Booster Club also sells caps. The club can buy a cap for $3.00. If the club
                sells a cap at a 50% increase, how much will they charge for a cap?

CT-69. Snack bars make their profit by selling each product for more than its purchase price. The operators of a snack bar purchase products at wholesale prices. To determine the selling price of an item, they increase the wholesale price of it by a certain percentage. This amount of increase is the **markup**.

Snack	Wholesale Unit Price
Chips	$0.25
Pretzel	$0.25
Hot Dog	$1.00
Fruit Bowl	$0.70
Sunflower Seeds	$0.35
Popcorn	$0.55
Candy Bar	$0.38
Bottled Water	$0.25
Soda	$0.25
Coffee	$0.25
Sports Drink	$0.50

Steve, the Snack Bar Committee chairperson, wants to make a profit of at least 40% on each item. Some of the items and their wholesale unit prices are listed in the table at right.

Determining the **selling price** of a $0.25 bag of chips is a two-step process.

a) Determine the amount of money represented by the 40% markup by finding 40% of $0.25.

$$\frac{\%}{100} = \frac{\text{part}}{\text{a whole}} \qquad \frac{40}{100} = \frac{m}{\$0.25}$$

b) Add the markup to the wholesale price to determine the selling price.

CT-70. Use the resource page or make a complete table. Use the work shown for the chips and the candy bar as a model. Show all of your work.

Item	Wholesale Unit Price	Markup at 40% Rate	Selling Price
Chips	$0.25	$\frac{40}{100} = \frac{m}{\$0.25}$ $m = \$0.10$	$0.25 + $0.10 = $0.35
Hot Dog	$1.00		
Fruit Bowl	$0.70		
Sunflower Seeds	$0.35		
Popcorn	$0.55		
Candy Bar	$0.38	$\frac{40}{100} = \frac{m}{\$0.38}$ $m = \$0.15$	$0.38 + $0.15 = $0.53

CT-71. Listed below are four wholesale unit prices. Calculate each selling price if the wholesale unit prices will be marked up 70%. Show your work.

a) $0.85

b) $1.25

c) $2.40

d) $0.95

CT-72.   Simplify the expressions. Write each whole number as a fraction greater than one, then add or subtract. Do not write your answers as mixed numbers; leave them in fraction form.

a) $2 + \frac{2}{3}$

b) $3 + \frac{2}{5}$

c) $5 - \frac{3}{4}$

d) $\frac{3}{8} - 2$

CT-73.   Write an equation for each of the following fraction bar models. Then find x.

a)

b)

CT-74.

```
                    MARKUP AND SELLING PRICES

The amount that the cost of an item will increase is called a MARKUP. This
increase is based on a percentage of the cost.

The SELLING PRICE is the sum of the original cost and the markup.

Example:
The wholesale price of a pen is $0.70. To ensure a profit, Angela must mark up the
wholesale price by 35%. Determine the markup and selling price.
```

$$\frac{\%}{100} = \frac{part}{a\ whole} \qquad \frac{35}{100} = \frac{m}{\$0.70} \qquad markup = \$0.2450 \approx \$0.25$$

$$selling\ price = wholesale + markup = \$0.70 + \$0.25 = \$0.95$$

In your Tool Kit highlight the two lines in the example that show how to find the markup and selling price.

CT-75.   Solve for x. Show your work.

a) $\frac{1}{6}x = 25$

b) $\frac{2}{3}x = \frac{1}{2}$

c) $\frac{3}{4}x = 9$

d) $12x = 4$

CT-76. Look at the outcome grid you made in problem CT-26 for rolling one green and one white die. Ellen is playing a game that requires her to roll the two dice and add together the values shown.

a) What is the fractional probability that her sum would equal 2? In other words, find P(2).

b) P(3) = ?   c) P(4) = ?   d) P(5) = ?   e) P(6) = ?

f) P(7) = ?   g) P(8) = ?   h) P(9) = ?   i) P(10) = ?

j) P(11) = ?   k) P(12) = ?

l) Do the answers in parts (a) through (k) show all the possible ways for two dice to land? If you were to add the fractional probabilities, what should the sum be? Check your results above by adding the answers from parts (a) through (k). If the sum does not equal the number that you think it should, check your outcome grid for errors and add again.

CT-77. Solve for x.

a) $2x - 9 = 3$ b) $0.25x = 12$

c) $2x - 6 = 10$ d) $\frac{5}{7} = \frac{x + 2}{20}$

CT-78. Daniel has a scale drawing of his patio that he needs to paint. He knows the width of the patio is 10 feet, but the scale drawing is in inches.

a) Find the length of the patio. Show your steps.

b) Find the area of the patio so Daniel knows how much paint to buy.

c) One can of patio paint covers 125 square feet. How many cans of paint will Daniel need?

CT-79. Joshua is saving $2 each week. If he starts with $5, how many weeks will it take for him to reach $34? Write an equation and solve it. A table or a graph may be helpful.

CT-80. Prepare another card for the class tournament.

CT-81.   Follow your teacher's directions for practicing mental math.

CT-82.   Consider which discount is better for each item.

    a)   Would you rather buy a $12 t-shirt that is advertised as 30% off or $\frac{1}{3}$ off? Why?

    b)   Would you rather buy a $50 glove that is advertised as 40% off or $\frac{1}{4}$ off? Why?

CT-83.   Cheryl is the manager of a furniture store which is having a 25% off sale. Joyce is an employee and Rhonda is a customer. Cheryl and Joyce also receive employee discounts on their purchases. The **discount**, a percent or fraction of the original price, is subtracted to find the final cost of the item. Copy and complete the table showing each person's discount as a percent, a decimal, and a fraction.

	Cheryl's Discount	Joyce's Discount	Rhonda's Discount
Percent	50%		
Decimal		0.40	
Fraction			

CT-84.   A rain coat costs $250. Find how much the coat will cost with the following discounts.

    a)   50%   b)   25%   c)   10%   d)   5%

CT-85. Kathy, the snack bar manager, needs to determine the end-of-tournament sale prices. One of the items to be discounted by 25% is a $1.40 hot dog. She asked Myrna and Fern to calculate the discounted prices for her. Kathy was pleased to find that Myrna and Fern, with their math teams, had accurately calculated the discounts in two different ways.

Myrna's Team		Fern's Team	
25% of $1.40 x = discount amount $\dfrac{\%}{100} = \dfrac{part}{whole}$		25% of $1.40 d = sale price 100% – discount (%)	
$\dfrac{25}{100} = \dfrac{x}{\$1.40}$	1)_____	100% – 25% = 75%	1)_____
x = $0.35	2)_____	$\dfrac{75}{100} = \dfrac{d}{\$1.40}$	2)_____
$1.40 – $0.35 = $1.05	3)_____	d = $1.05	3)_____
Sale price is $1.05.		Sale price is $1.05.	

a) Explain what Myrna's team did in each of their steps (1 through 3) to find the sale price of the hot dogs.

b) Explain what Fern's team did in each of their steps (1 through 3) to find the sale price of the hot dogs.

c) Compare the two methods above. How are they different?

CT-86. Find the discount and sale price of the items below. Round up to the nearest cent. Show your work. Use both methods from problem CT-85 for part (a). Use either method for parts (b) and (c).

a) Price: $25.75
   Discount: 35%

b) Price: $5.99
   Discount: 25%

c) Price: $0.95
   Discount: 30%

CT-87.   Dave was a "shop-till-you-drop" kind of person and had a great time at the mall.

a)   He purchased a $45 tie at 40% off. Calculate the selling price. How much did he save?

b)   He purchased a pair of $65 pants at 30% off. Calculate the selling price. How much did he save?

c)   He also purchased an $84 dress for his wife at one-third off. Calculate the selling price. How much did he save?

d)   How much did Dave spend on all his purchases? How much did he save?

CT-88.

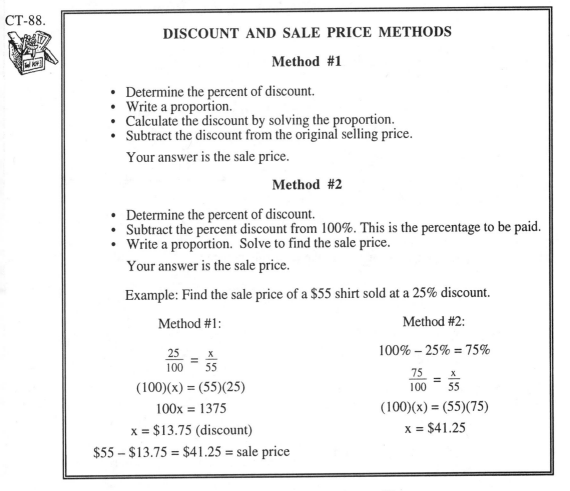

DISCOUNT AND SALE PRICE METHODS

Method #1

- Determine the percent of discount.
- Write a proportion.
- Calculate the discount by solving the proportion.
- Subtract the discount from the original selling price.

Your answer is the sale price.

Method #2

- Determine the percent of discount.
- Subtract the percent discount from 100%. This is the percentage to be paid.
- Write a proportion. Solve to find the sale price.

Your answer is the sale price.

Example: Find the sale price of a $55 shirt sold at a 25% discount.

Method #1:

$$\frac{25}{100} = \frac{x}{55}$$
$$(100)(x) = (55)(25)$$
$$100x = 1375$$
$$x = \$13.75 \text{ (discount)}$$
$$\$55 - \$13.75 = \$41.25 = \text{sale price}$$

Method #2:

$$100\% - 25\% = 75\%$$
$$\frac{75}{100} = \frac{x}{55}$$
$$(100)(x) = (55)(75)$$
$$x = \$41.25$$

In your Tool Kit highlight the steps in the method you will use.

CT-89.   Find the sale price of a $ 0.65 bag of peanuts sold at a 30% discount. Do the problem twice, using each method once.

CT-90.   Find the new sale prices for the following snack bar items. For the final few hours of the tournament, the discount will be 45%. Round your answer to the nearest cent.

a)   Chips: $0.35   b)   Hot Dog: $1.40

c)   Popcorn: $0.77   d)   Candy Bar: $0.53

e)   Do these seem like prices a snack bar would charge? Why or why not? What do you think the snack bar manager would do about the awkward prices?

CT-91.   Kaitlin's family spent $60.25 at the fair. If it cost $10 for all of them to get in, and the tickets for the rides were $0.75 each, how many rides did the family go on? Write and solve an equation to represent this problem. Be sure to answer in a complete sentence.

CT-92.   Find the perimeter and area of the two triangles below.

a)   b)

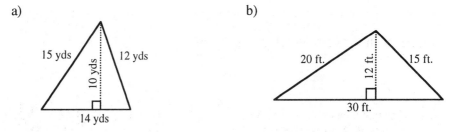

CT-93.   Write the reciprocal of each of the following numbers.

a)   5   b) $\frac{4}{5}$ c) $\frac{6}{7}$

d) $\frac{2}{3}$ e)   7   f) $1\frac{1}{3}$

CT-94. Rob lives in northern Arizona and recorded the following high and low temperatures for a two-week period last winter. (Temperatures are recorded in degrees Celsius.)

Day	1	2	3	4	5	6	7	8	9	10	11	12	13	14
Low Temperature	-8	-6	-6	-5	-2	4	12	10	8	0	-1	-3	-9	-8
High Temperature	4	6	8	8	10	10	16	16	15	9	4	6	-1	-5

a) Find the mean, median, and mode for the low temperatures.

b) Which average best represents the low temperatures? Explain.

c) Find the range for the low temperatures. What does the range indicate about the temperatures?

d) Find the range, mean, median, and mode for the high temperatures.

CT-95. Prepare another card for the class tournament.

CT-96. A regular newspaper measures 60.96 centimeters by 38.1 centimeters. The largest newspaper was the *HetVolk*, printed in Belgium in 1993. It measured 142 centimeters by 99.5 centimeters. How many times larger was the area of *HetVolk* than a regular newspaper?

CT-97. Solve the following problems.

a) Eight is what percent of 40?

b) Fifteen is 30% of what number?

c) What is 42% of 87?

d) Sixteen is what percent of 157?

CT-98. Find the <u>differences</u> between the following values.

a) 217 and -198

b) $1\frac{2}{3}$ and $\frac{3}{4}$

c) $0.59 and $1.25

CT-99. Myrna and Fern's teams are practicing for the class tournament by giving each other problems to solve. Each team solved this problem: A shirt purchased wholesale for $15 has been marked up 80%. What is the new price?

<table>
<tr><td align="center">Myrna's Team</td><td align="center">Fern's Team</td></tr>
</table>

Myrna's Team

$$\frac{80}{100} = \frac{x}{\$15.00}$$

$100x = 1200$

$x = \$12.00$

$\$15.00 + \$12.00 = \$27.00$

Fern's Team

$100\% + 80\%$ (increase) $= 180\%$

$$\frac{180}{100} = \frac{x}{15.00}$$

$100x = 2700$

$x = \$27.00$

a) Compare the two solution methods. How are they different? Explain in complete sentences.

b) How are the methods above similar to those used in problem CT-85? How are the methods different? Explain in complete sentences.

c) Which method do you prefer? Why? Explain in complete sentences.

CT-100.

Duane is an old-timer who helps out around the baseball field. Melissa started talking to him and discovered some interesting facts. When Duane was a child, frozen juice bar were 2¢. Now they are 60¢. Matinee movies were $0.75. Now they are $4.50. Bread was 24¢ for a small loaf. Now it is $2.19. Gasoline was 19¢ per gallon. Now it is $1.58 per gallon.

Below is how to find the percent increase of a frozen juice bar.

1) Find the amount of increase: 60¢ – 2¢ = 58¢

2) Set up a proportion to find the percent, following the formula:

$$\frac{58 \text{ (amount of increase)}}{2 \text{ (original price)}} = \frac{x \text{ (percent)}}{100}$$

3) Solve the proportion: $58 \cdot 100 = 2x \implies 5800 = 2x \implies 2900 = x$

The price of this frozen juice bar has increased by 2900%!

Find the percentage increase for the other items listed above.

CT-101. Sometimes prices go down. Duane remembers when he bought his first calculator for $110. If calculators are now available for $5.75, what is the percentage decrease? Remember to compare the difference to the starting amount.

CT-102. Mighty Max weighed in at 135 pounds for wrestling. By the time the season ended, he weighed 128 pounds. What was the percentage decrease of his weight?

CT-103. Find the percentage increase or decrease of each of the following items:

Item	Original Price	Current Price	Percentage Increase or Decrease
Milk	$0.25	$2.25	
Candy Bar	5¢	55¢	
Computer	$2000	$1200	
Hamburger	19¢	89¢	

CT-104. What is the meaning of a percentage increase that is greater than 100%?

CT-105.

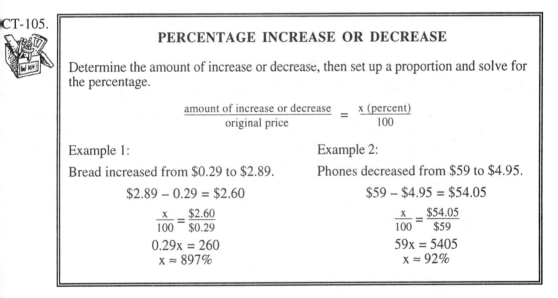

PERCENTAGE INCREASE OR DECREASE

Determine the amount of increase or decrease, then set up a proportion and solve for the percentage.

$$\frac{\text{amount of increase or decrease}}{\text{original price}} = \frac{x\ (\text{percent})}{100}$$

Example 1:

Bread increased from $0.29 to $2.89.

$2.89 - 0.29 = $2.60

$$\frac{x}{100} = \frac{\$2.60}{\$0.29}$$

$0.29x = 260$

$x \approx 897\%$

Example 2:

Phones decreased from $59 to $4.95.

$59 - $4.95 = $54.05

$$\frac{x}{100} = \frac{\$54.05}{\$59}$$

$59x = 5405$

$x \approx 92\%$

Highlight the proportion you use to find the amount of increase or decrease in your Tool Kit.

CT-106. A tank top decreased in price from $12.50 to $10.50. What is the percentage decrease?

CT-107. The town's population has grown from 11,567 to 28,760 over a period of fifteen years. By approximately what percent has the town grown in that time?

CT-108. One item for sale in the snack bar is a miniature glove that gets larger when soaked in water. The package says its size increases 600%. If the glove is two inches long, how long will it be once it is put in water?

CT-109. Carol is buying a hat for $9.95 with a sales tax of 5%. What will be the total cost after tax is added?

CT-110. Complete the following table.

Problem	What is missing? (part, whole, or %)	Write a proportion.	Solve for x.
What percent of 70 is 14?			
Twelve is 3% of what number?			
25% of 48 is what number?			

CT-111. Prepare another card for the class tournament.

T-112.

FORMULAS

A **formula** is a shorthand way of writing a general mathematical statement or rule. When writing formulas, variables are assigned to represent the various parts of the rule or statement.

Write a formula for each of the following statements in your Tool Kit to the right of the double-lined box.

a) One-sixth of your Earth weight is your weight on the Moon. Let e represent Earth weight and m represent Moon weight.

b) Distance is equal to the rate of speed times the time it takes to travel. Use d for distance, r for rate of speed, and t for the time it takes to travel.

c) The interest (dollars you earn) for a savings account that pays simple interest is equal to the amount of money deposited (principal) times the percentage rate times the amount of time the money is invested. Use I for interest, P for principal, r for rate, and t for time.

d) The circumference of a circle is the product of the diameter and π. Use C for circumference and d for diameter.

e) A batting average is found by taking the total hits made and dividing it by all of the times at bat (excepting walks, hit batters, and sacrifices). Use H for hits and AB for times at bat.

T-113. Sometimes an equation has two or more variables. Look at each pair of problems below. How are they alike? How are they different? In each equation the goal is to solve for x. Work with a partner and solve each equation. Assume that none of the variables equal zero.

a) $5x + 4 = 14$ and $mx + 4 = 14$

b) $2x + 5 = 6$ and $nx + 5 = 6$

c) $3x - 8 = 16$ and $cx - 8 = 16$

T-114. Solve the equations below. For equations with more than one variable, you may want to circle the variable for which you are solving. This will help remind you that it is the variable you want left by itself.

a) Solve for x: $\$6.25x = \$50.$ b) Solve for x: $\$6.25x = y.$

c) Solve for r: $D = rt$ d) Solve for d: $C = \pi d$

e) Solve for y: $x = ay$ f) Solve for r: $d = 2r$

g) Solve for a: $F = ma$

CT-115.   Look back in your Tool Kit and find the formula for the area of a trapezoid.

   a)   Write the formula for the area of a trapezoid.

   b)   Find the area of the trapezoid at right.

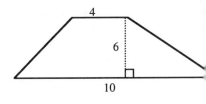

CT-116.   Calculate the area of each of these trapezoids. Show all your steps.

   a)   b)

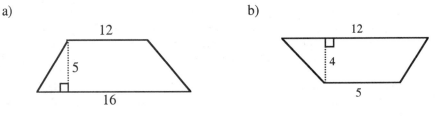

CT-117.   Work with your partner. Give your partner step-by-step instructions for how to solve pa
           (a), and he or she will record what you say. Exchange roles for part (b).

   a)   6x + 36 = 150   b) $3.65x + $0.25 = $11.20

CT-118.   Perform the following unit conversions. Remember you can use your Tool Kit.

   a)   Explain how to convert 72 inches into feet.

   b)   Explain how to convert 192 ounces into pounds.

   c)   Tim wrote, "To change feet into miles, multiply by 5,280." Carolan said, "Tim,
         you're way off! You divide by 5,280." Who is correct? How do you know?

CT-119.   Use the equation $y = 2x + 3$ to find the values for y in the table below.

x	-3	-1	0	2	4
y					

   a)   Graph it.

   b)   What is the x-intercept?

   c)   What is the y-intercept?

CT-120. Solve for x.

   a) $4x + 6 = 26$ b) $ax + 6 = 26$

   c) $15x = 135$ d) $gx = 135$

   e) $\$0.25x + \$4.50 = \$14.75$ f) $\frac{5}{6}x = 35$

CT-121. A box contains 15 yellow, 15 orange, and 15 green
         tennis balls. If Izzy draws a tennis ball at random out of
         the box, what is the probability that he drew either a
         green or an orange tennis ball? Show your work and
         express your answer as a percent.

CT-122. Find the designated areas of the following circle. The
         shaded region is one-eighth of the circle.

   a)   What is the area of the unshaded region of the
        circle?

   b)   What is the area of the shaded region?

   c)   In a few sentences explain each of the steps you
        followed to answer parts (a) and (b).

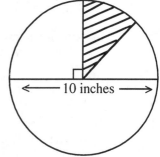

CT-123. Solve for x.

   a) $45x = 630$ b) $2(48 + x) = 160$ c) $0.32x = 175$

CT-124. Solve for the indicated variable.

   a)   Solve for w :   b)   Solve for t :   c)   Solve for b :

        $s = w + m$. $d = rt$. $A = \frac{1}{2} bh$.

CT-125. Prepare another card for the class tournament.

CT-126. Write down the positive integers as shown below. Which column will contain the number 500 ?

$$
\begin{array}{rrr}
1 & 2 & 3 \\
6 & 5 & 4 \\
 & 7 & 8 & 9 \\
12 & 11 & 10 \\
\end{array}
$$

CT-127. Follow your teacher's directions for practicing mental math. Write the new strategy you learned.

CT-128. Howie is driving from Minneapolis to Indianapolis. He plans to drive 65 miles per hour. How far can he travel in 7 hours? Copy and complete the table below.

Time (hours)	1	2	4	7	9
Distance (miles)					

a) Do you see a pattern in the table to help you find a rule? What was your rule or formula? Write it in the form "Distance Traveled = ..."

b) If Minneapolis is 575 miles from Indianapolis, how long will it take him to drive there at 65 miles per hour?

c) If Howie drove 70 miles per hour for 7 hours, how far would he travel?

CT-129. Howie knows it takes approximately 4 hours to drive from Madison to Des Moines, a distance of about 275 miles. How fast must he travel to drive the distance within 4 hours? Use your formula to help you.

a) What is t ?

b) What is d ?

c) Fill in the numbers you know and solve your equation to let Howie know how fast he has to drive.

CT-130. Next year, teams will be invited to a math tournament from all over the state. To help them decide if they want to enter the tournament, a driving distance time chart will be included in the announcement.

Copy the driving distance time chart and use the formula you wrote in problem CT-128 to fill in the missing information.

City	Distance (miles)	Rate of Speed (mph)	Time (hours)
West Valley		70	4.5
Willow Springs	183	70	
Center City	247		3.8
Highland Park	48	60	

CT-131. Your teacher recently announced that the class mathematics tournament would take place in a few days. You and your classmates have had the opportunity to demonstrate the math proficiency you have been developing over the school year by writing math problems with their solutions. The object of the tournament is to answer the problems correctly to earn as many points as you can for your team.

Tomorrow is the tournament day! Follow the instructions below to prepare for the tournament.

a) Using the review cards you have created throughout this chapter, select the two cards you think are your best. Make sure that your solutions are correct and complete.

b) Exchange these cards with a partner. Help each other ensure that all the information and the solutions on your cards are correct.

c) Work together to select the best cards from the team to give to your teacher. Your teacher will tell you how many cards to select.

d) Give these cards to your teacher.

e) Write "Cards have been selected" on your paper.

CT-132.

DISTANCE, RATE, TIME

DISTANCE (d) equals the product of the rate of speed (r) and the time (t).

$$d = r \cdot t$$

Example: Find the rate of speed of a passenger car if the distance traveled is 572 miles and the time elapsed is 11 hours.

$$572 \text{ miles} = r \cdot 11 \text{ hours} \implies \frac{572 \text{ miles}}{11 \text{ hours}} = \text{rate} \implies 52 \text{ miles/hour} = \text{rate}$$

Make these notes in your Tool Kit to the right of the double-lined box.

Give two real-world examples when you could use this distance formula.

CT-133. Solve the following problems.

a) Find the time if the distance is 157.5 miles and the speed is 63 mph.

b) Find the distance if the speed is 67 mph and the time is 3.5 hours.

CT-134. Find the batting average for Dynamic David. He had 20 hits in 62 at bats.

CT-135. Solve the problems below.

a) $\frac{3}{8}x = 12$

b) $\frac{5}{6} \div \frac{2}{5}$

c) How much is a markup of 25% on a price of $6.99?

CT-136. A triangular shaped playground has a height of 23 meters and a base of 32 meters. Write the area formula for a triangle and use this to determine the area of the playground.

CT-137. Ellen is playing a game that requires her to roll two dice and add them together. Use the outcome grid you made in problem CT-26 for rolling one green die and one white die to answer the following questions.

a) What is the probability of rolling 7 or larger? P(7 or larger) = ?

b) What is the probability of rolling 6 or less? P(6 or less) = ?

c) What is the probability of rolling an odd or an even number? P(even or odd) = ?

d) What is the probability of rolling 1? P(1) = ?

e) What is the probability of rolling 4 or 5? P(4 or 5) = ?

f) Trixie wants to play a game in which she wins with a sum of 3 or 6 and you win with a sum of 2 or 12. She says this is fair because you both have two winning numbers. Is this game fair? Explain.

CT-138. Use the resource page or copy the table below, then simplify each fraction by eliminating Giant **1**s. Rewrite your answer using exponents if necessary. The first one is done for you.

	Original Expression	Eliminate Common Factors	Simplified Expression
a)	$\dfrac{6 \cdot x \cdot x}{3 \cdot x \cdot x \cdot x \cdot x}$	$\dfrac{2 \cdot \cancel{3} \cdot \cancel{x} \cdot \cancel{x}}{\cancel{3} \cdot \cancel{x} \cdot \cancel{x} \cdot x \cdot x}$	$\dfrac{2}{x^2}$
b)	$\dfrac{x \cdot x \cdot x}{x}$		
c)	$\dfrac{21 \cdot x \cdot x \cdot x}{7 \cdot x}$		
d)	$\dfrac{a \cdot a \cdot a \cdot b}{a \cdot b}$		
e)	$\dfrac{16\pi r^2}{4r}$		

CT-139. Rewrite the following products using exponents.

a) $4y \cdot 4y \cdot 4y \cdot 4y$

b) $3x \cdot 3x \cdot 3x$

c) $4a \cdot 3a$

d) $3ab \cdot 4ab^2$

CT-140. **Rules for the Class Tournament**

Your teacher will assign you to a team and give you a color-coded card with a number. The color represents your team. The number is your player number. When the teacher calls your number, it will be your turn to work with another student on your team to answer a question correctly.

Your teacher will assign your team a space on the chalk or white board. Be sure you work in that space only. Follow all rules concerning replacing the chalk or marker, circling the answer, and erasing your work after the points have been awarded. You will lose points if you forget.

• Appoint a scorekeeper for your team.

• When you are a member of the audience, remember that yelling or blurting out an answer will cause your team to lose points.

• Your teacher will tell you how many points will be awarded for correct solutions and how many points will be deducted for not following the rules.

• Consult with your teammates and make sure you all understand the answer. Remember to ask the teacher for clarification if you all have the same question.

• If there are no further questions, you are ready to play. Good luck!

CT-141. To promote the tournament Ida made a rectangular banner with a length of 320 centimeters and a width of 450 centimeters. Then other students made more flags based on Ida's. For each of the other flags, calculate the new dimensions, then calculate the new perimeter and area.

a) Each dimension of Amy's flag is 25% larger than Ida's.

b) Each dimension of Maria's flag is 30% smaller than Ida's.

c) Each dimension of Kristyn's flag is $1\frac{1}{2}$ times larger than Ida's.

CT-142. Design a dart board for a dart tournament that meets the following conditions.

a) $\frac{1}{4}$ is red

b) 15% is green

c) 0.4 is yellow

d) the rest is blue

e) If you threw 100 darts and they all hit the board, what is the probability of hitting:

i) red? ii) green? iii) yellow? iv) blue?

f) If you threw 120 darts and they all hit the board, how many darts would hit each color?

i) red ii) green iii) yellow iv) blue

CT-143. Anita charges $12.00 to mow her neighbor's lawn. Whenever her neighbor wants additional work done on the yard, Anita charges $4.50 per hour. How many extra hours did she work if the total amount she charged the neighbor was $43.50? Write and solve an equation to answer the question.

CT-144. Anita's mother insists that she put 30% of her earnings into a college fund. Find the total amount she puts into the fund for 3 mowings and five extra hours of yard work.

CT-145. Solve for x. Show your work.

a) $x + 32 = 5x - 12$ b) $100 = 5(2x + 9)$

c) $10x = 2(x + 4)$ d) $4(3x - 8) = 2x + 21$

CT-146. You decide to visit the Mathematical Amusement Park again on a special plan. Your choices are Plan 1, in which you pay $7.50 to enter the park and $1.10 per ride, or Plan 2, in which you pay $12.50 to enter the park and $0.60 per ride. Write an equation to determine the number of rides that would make the total cost equal for the two plans. Then solve the equation.

CT-147. There are 18 chocolate chip cookies, 12 oatmeal cookies, and 10 raisin cookies in a cookie jar. If Miguel takes a cookie from the jar without looking, what is the probability that he does <u>not</u> get a chocolate chip cookie? Show work to support your answer.

CT-148. Kirby has $75 in a savings account. He had only $55 in the account 4 weeks ago. He wants to buy a guitar for $185. Assume he has been saving the same amount of money each week.

a)   At what rate is he saving money each week?

b)   Copy the data table below and fill in the account totals for each week.

Time (x) in weeks	-4	-3	-2	-1	0	1	2	3
Amount (y) in dollars	$55				$75			

c)   Graph this situation.

d)   Use the table or the graph to determine when the amount in his account will be $185.

e)   Determine when Kirby started saving money.

CT-149. Find the following distances, rates, or times.

Distance	Rate of Speed	Time
	45 mph	1.5 hours
362 miles	68 mph	
128 miles		2.5 hours
72 miles		$\frac{3}{4}$ hours

CT-150. A rectangle is graphed so that two of the sides are on the x- and y-axes and the vertex opposite the origin is at (-4, 6). Graph the rectangle.

a) In which quadrant is the rectangle?

b) What are the dimensions of the rectangle?

c) If the dimensions are increased by 40% and two sides of the rectangle stay on the x- and y-axes, what are the coordinates of the vertex opposite the origin?

d) What is the percentage increase of the perimeter and the percentage increase of the area?

CT-151. A floor plan for the snack bar is shown at right, but it is too large. Reduce the figure by reducing all the measurements by 30%. (All measurements are given in feet.) Then calculate the percentage decrease of the new area.

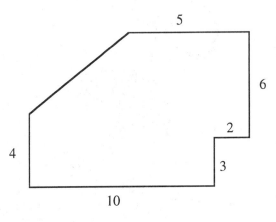

CT-152. **What We Have Done in This Chapter**

Below is a list of the Tool Kit entries from this chapter.

- CT-22   Reciprocal or Multiplicative Inverse
- CT-41   Solving Equations with Fractional Coefficients
- CT-48   Division of Fractions
- CT-57   Simple Interest
- CT-58   Compound Interest
- CT-74   Markup and Selling Prices
- CT-88   Discount and Sale Price Methods
- CT-105   Percentage Increase or Decrease
- CT-112   Formulas
- CT-132   Distance, Rate, Time

Review all the entries and read the notes you made in your Tool Kit. Make a list of any questions, terms, or notes you do not understand. Ask your partner or study team members for help. If anything is still unclear, ask your teacher.

Gold Strike!

at Dried Up Creek

Chapter 8

Chapter 8
Gold Strike At Dried-Up Creek:
THE PYTHAGOREAN THEOREM, SURFACE AREA, AND VOLUME

In this chapter you will work with right triangles and use them to solve complex problems. You will also work with cubes and nets to learn about surface area and volume.

In this chapter you will have the opportunity to:

- identify right triangles.

- develop and use the Pythagorean Theorem.

- use the technique of subproblems to solve complex problems.

- find the surface area and volume of prisms and cylinders.

Read the problem below, but **do not try to solve it now**. What you learn over the next few days wil enable you to solve it.

GS-0.   **The Mine Shaft**

Sourdough Sam was given a gold mine. To get the gold, Sourdough Sam's mining company will build a sturdy entry platform for the new mine shaft. The platform will be a rectangular prism 4 feet high with a base 20 feet by 15 feet. The concrete for the platform will be poured around a cylindrical hole 6 feet in diameter. The miners will be lowered through the hole to get to the vein of gold. Sam needs to know how many cubic feet of concrete to order and how much it will weigh.

Number Sense		
Algebra and Functions		
Mathematical Reasoning		
Measurement and Geometry		
Statistics, Data Analysis, & Probability		

Chapter 8

Gold Strike At Dried-Up Creek:

THE PYTHAGOREAN THEOREM, SURFACE AREA, AND VOLUME

GS-1.   Calculate.

a) $3^2 + 4^2$ b) 5^2 c) $5^2 + 12^2$ d) 13^2

GS-2.

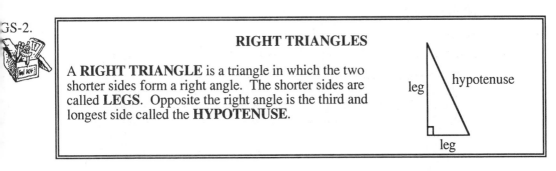

RIGHT TRIANGLES

A **RIGHT TRIANGLE** is a triangle in which the two shorter sides form a right angle. The shorter sides are called **LEGS**. Opposite the right angle is the third and longest side called the **HYPOTENUSE**.

Make these notes in your Tool Kit to the right of the double-lined box.

a)   Highlight "the shorter sides are called legs" and "longest side called the hypotenuse."

b)   How many degrees are in a right angle?

GS-3.   Mr. Wrangler gave each of his sons, Luke and Duke, square-shaped property around triangular lakes. He knew Luke wanted more shoreline, so he gave Luke two smaller pieces on the shorter sides of the lakes. Duke wanted less shoreline and lots of wide open space. Therefore, his father gave him the big square of land on the long side. Luke was sure he had more land because he had two pieces of land on each lake. Duke's piece on the lake was largest, so he was sure he had more.

Using the diagram at right, help Luke and Duke settle their disagreement.

a)   What shape is the lake?

b)   Copy the table below. You will also need this table for the next problem. Find the area of each square around Lake 1. Record the data in the table.

c)   Compare the sum of the area of Luke's land with the area of Duke's land. Was it split fairly?

| Lake | Luke's Areas | | | Duke's |
	Square 1	Square 2	Total Area	Square Area
1				
2				
3				

GS-4.   Luke and Duke received property around two other lakes on the Wrangler property. Their land here is shaped like the property around Lake 1.

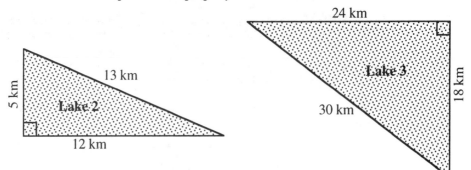

a)   Draw Lakes 2 and 3 and sketch the surrounding square plots of land. Remember that Luke has two pieces of land on the shorter sides of each lake. Duke has one piece of land on the longest side of each lake. Label each plot of land with the name of the owner. What is the shape of each lake?

b)   Find the area of each square around Lakes 2 and 3. Record the data in the table from the previous problem.

c)   Compare the sum of the areas each brother received. Was the land split fairly?

GS-5.   Mr. Wrangler used a formula to ensure the land would be split fairly. The formula describes the relationship between the legs and hypotenuse of any right triangle. Answer the following questions using the diagram and table information for Lake 1.

a)   How does the <u>sum</u> of the squares of the leg lengths compare with the square of the length of the hypotenuse?

b)   Write an equation describing the relationship of the two shorter legs and the hypotenuse. This formula is called the **Pythagorean Theorem**.

c)   If you were given the area of one of the square pieces of land, how would you find the length of the side?

d)   Suppose one of the squares had an area of 64 km². What is the length of its side, that is, the distance along that portion of the lake?

GS-6.   This activity will help confirm the relationship between the legs and the hypotenuse of a right triangle.

a)   Copy the table below, leaving room to fill in the blanks.

triangle	length of leg 1	length of leg 2	length of hypotenuse	$(\text{length of leg 1})^2$ $+$ $(\text{length of leg 2})^2$	$(\text{length of hypotenuse})^2$	equal?
1)	5	12				
2)	6	8				
3)	9	.12				

>>Problem continues on the next page.>>

b)   On graph paper, use a ruler to <u>carefully</u> draw right triangles that have the leg lengths in the table. Use the side of one square of graph paper as one unit.

c)   Measure the length of each hypotenuse using a graph paper ruler. Record these lengths in your chart. Check your measurements with your study team.

d)   Complete the table by squaring the leg lengths and the hypotenuse length. Then check your answers with your study team.

e)   Does the relationship between the numbers in the last column in the table match the one described by the Pythagorean Theorem?

GS-7.   Use the Pythagorean Theorem to determine whether the lengths listed below form a right triangle. Explain your reasoning.

a)   15 feet, 36 feet, and 39 feet

b)   20 inches, 21 inches, and 29 inches

c)   8 yards, 9 yards, and 12 yards

d)   4 meters, 7 meters, and 8 meters

GS-8.

MEASUREMENT IN DIFFERENT DIMENSIONS

Measurements in one dimension are labeled as cm, ft, etc.

_____

1 foot

Measurements in two dimensions are labeled as cm^2, ft^2, etc.

1 foot   1 ft x 1 ft = 1 ft^2

1 foot

Measurements in three dimensions are labeled as cm^3, ft^3, etc.

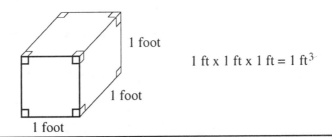

1 foot

1 ft x 1 ft x 1 ft = 1 ft^3

1 foot

1 foot

Make these notes in your Tool Kit to the right of the double-lined box.

Highlight each shape and the corresponding units.

GS-9.

┌───┐
│   │
│   **PYTHAGOREAN THEOREM**   │

The **PYTHAGOREAN THEOREM** states that for any right triangle, the sum of the squares of the lengths of the legs is equal to the square of the length of the hypotenuse.

(leg 1)^2 + (leg 2)^2 = (hypotenuse)^2

Example:

$$(3)^2 + (4)^2 = (x)^2$$
$$9 + 16 = (x)^2$$
$$25 = (x)^2$$
$$5 = x$$

└───┘

Make these notes in your Tool Kit to the right of the double-lined box.

a)   Highlight the formula for the Pythagorean Theorem.

b)   Is it possible to find the length of one leg if you are given the lengths of the other leg and the hypotenuse? If so, how?

GS-10.   Find the areas of the following shapes. If you can, also find the perimeters. If you cannot explain why you cannot.

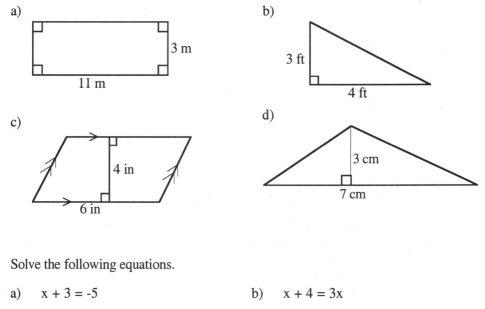

a)

3 m

11 m

b)

3 ft

4 ft

c)

4 in

6 in

d)

3 cm

7 cm

GS-11.   Solve the following equations.

a)   x + 3 = -5

b)   x + 4 = 3x

c)   2x – 5 = -3

d)   2x – 1.5 = 7

GS-12. The Wild West Frontier Park now offers an unlimited day pass. For $29.00, visitors can go on as many rides as they want. The original plan charged visitors $8.75 to enter the park plus $2.25 for each ride. Write an equation to determine the number of rides that would make the total cost equal for the two plans. Solve the equation.

GS-13. Convert the following percents to decimals.

a)   35%   b)   17%   c)   4%

d)   2.5%   e)   65.8%   f)   0.09%

GS-14. Write out the following expressions without exponents and compute their values.

a) 2^2 b) 2^3 c) 4^2

d) 3^4 e) 7^3 f) 5^4

GS-15. Jack noticed there was a sale on Quadrunners. The salesperson said the company was cutting the price for that weekend, so Jack got an 8% discount.

a)   If the usual price of the Quadrunner was $4298, what amount did Jack pay with the 8% discount?

b)   If the store sold three Quadrunners that weekend, how much money was saved in all by the three customers?

GS-16. Write the inverse operation that will "undo" each of the operations below. Operations that undo another operation are called **inverse operations**.

a)   addition   b)   division   c)   subtraction

d)   distributing   e)   multiplication   f)   factoring

GS-17. Copy and complete the following table or use the resource page. Addition and subtraction are each used twice, once each way.

First #	What was done to the first number to get the second number?	Second #	What can be done to the second number to get the first number again?
60		2	
x		3x	
47		40	
1		97	
36		6	

What do the two columns you filled out have in common? What is different about them?

GS-18.   Use graph paper to complete the following problems.

a)   How many different rectangles with whole number dimensions can you make that have an area of 12 square units? Sketch them on graph paper and label their dimensions.

b)   Can you make a square with an area of 12 if you use whole numbers for the length of the sides? If so, what are its dimensions? If not, explain why not.

c)   How many different rectangles that have an area of 16 can you make using whole numbers for the length and width? Sketch them on graph paper and label their dimensions.

d)   Can you make a square with an area of 16? If so, what are its dimensions? If not, explain why not.

e)   How many different rectangles with whole number dimensions can you make that have an area of 40? Sketch them on graph paper and label their dimensions.

f)   Can you make a square with whole number dimensions that has an area of 40? If so, what are its dimensions? If not, explain why not.

g)   What is the next largest area after 40 for which you could make a square with side lengths that are whole numbers? What are its dimensions?

h)   What is the next smallest area under 40 for which you could make a square with side lengths that are whole numbers? What are its dimensions?

GS-19.   Area numbers that can make a square are called square numbers or **perfect squares**. If the following numbers are perfect squares, list the dimensions of the square they make.

a)   Is 16 a perfect square?   b)   Is 54 a perfect square?

c)   Is 1 a perfect square?   d)   Is 81 a perfect square?

GS-20.   Complete a table like the one below to record all the square numbers (perfect squares) from 1 to 100.

Side Lengths of the Square	1	2	3	4	5	6	7	8	9	10	x
Area of the Square											

GS-21.   Study the example shown at right. It contains a mathematical symbol that might be new to you.

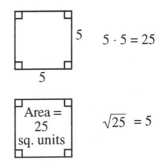

5 · 5 = 25

a)   Copy the new mathematical symbol.

b)   What does the √ symbol indicate should be done to the square area, 25?

Area = 25 sq. units

$\sqrt{25} = 5$

c)   What is the name of this symbol?

This is "unsquaring" or the inverse of squaring.

GS-22.   Just as $)\overline{}$ means dividing and is the inverse of multiplying, √ is a mathematical symbol that tells us to do the inverse of squaring. When the area of a square is given, we "unsquare" it to find the dimensions (that is, the lengths of the sides of the square). The inverse of squaring is called the **square root**. To show "unsquaring" or finding the square root, use a **radical sign**, √ .

a)   Sketch a square. Label the area 36 square units. Do not label its dimensions.

b)   Write the area under a √ . This means that we want to know the dimensions of a square with an area of 36. We are going to find the square root of 36.

c)   What are the lengths of the sides of the square you drew in part (a)?

d)   Use your expression with the √ in part (b) and your answer in part (c) to write an equation.

GS-23.   Copy each radical expression below and simplify it by finding the square root. (How long are the sides of squares with these areas?)

a) $\sqrt{49}$ b) $\sqrt{100}$ c) $\sqrt{144}$ d) $\sqrt{64}$

GS-24.

SQUARING AND SQUARE ROOT

When a number or variable is multiplied by itself, it is said to be **SQUARED**.

For example, $6 \cdot 6 = 6^2 = 36$, $a \cdot a = a^2$.

The **SQUARE ROOT** of a number or variable is the factor that when multiplied by itself results in the given number. Use a radical sign, $\sqrt{}$, to show this operation.

For example, $\sqrt{49}$ is read as "the square root of 49" and means, "Find the positive number that multiplied by itself equals 49." $\sqrt{49} = 7$, since $7 \cdot 7 = 49$.

When finding the area of a square you are squaring the number that represents the side length. When the area of a square is known, you determine its dimensions by finding the square root of a number.

Make these notes in your Tool Kit to the right of the double-lined box.

a) List two other pairs of mathematical operations that are inverses (opposites) of each other.

b) Highlight the information in the Tool Kit that tells you how to read the square root sign.

GS-25. Find each square root. Write your answer as an equation.

a) $\sqrt{81}$ b) $\sqrt{16}$ c) $\sqrt{25}$ d) $\sqrt{121}$

GS-26.

BASES AND EXPONENTS

Bases and exponents are used to write a number or expression in **exponential form**: a^n. The **BASE**, a, is a factor (number or variable expression) raised to a power. The **EXPONENT**, n, is sometimes called the power and indicates how many times the base is used as a factor.

In general, a^n means a multiplied by itself n times. For example, 2^4 means $2 \cdot 2 \cdot 2 \cdot 2$. The base is 2 and the exponent is 4.

Make these notes in your Tool Kit to the right of the double-lined box.

Write another example of a number in exponential form.

GS-27. Simplify, then name the base and the exponent.

a) 3^7 b) 8^5 c) $5(9-6)^3$

GS-28.   Ann is measuring some fabric pieces for a quilt. Use the Pythagorean Theorem to help
         her find each of the missing lengths below:

a)

32 in.

24 in.

b)

33 ft

44 ft

c)

25 cm

60 cm

d)

120 m

35 m

GS-29.   Determine the positive value that makes each equation true.

a)   If $x^2 = 36$,
     x = ?

b)   If $x^2 = 65$,
     x = ?

c)   If $x^2 = 84$,
     x = ?

d)   If $x^2 = 13$,
     x = ?

GS-30.   Sourdough Sam was in the hills prospecting for
         gold when he ran out of water. He walked two
         miles west, where he found a stream. He followed
         the stream north three miles. He looked down and
         saw something glittering. Gold! He had left all of
         his prospecting gear back at his campsite, so he
         walked directly back to it. How far did he have to
         go?

a)   Copy the diagram at right and use the
     Pythagorean Theorem to write an equation
     represented by the triangle to solve the problem.

b)   Solve your equation to find out how far away
     Sam's campsite is.

gold

x

3 mi.

stream

2 mi.

campsite

GS-31.   Sam decided to hide the gold where no one else would find it. He

          walked to a nearby tree to use it as a reference point, then went
          eighteen paces east and fifteen paces south. How far from the tree
          did Sam bury the gold?

          a)   Draw a diagram and label it.

          b)   Write and solve an equation to find how far from the tree he
                buried the gold.

GS-32.   Twin brothers Clem and Clyde are

          lookouts for the prospectors. One
          day, Clem climbed to the top of a
          75-foot vertical cliff to get a better
          look. He threw a 96-foot rope to
          Clyde. If the rope was stretched
          tightly from Clyde's feet to Clem's
          feet, how far from the base of the
          cliff is Clyde standing? Draw a
          diagram and label it. Use the
          Pythagorean Theorem to write an
          equation and solve it. Write a
          complete sentence that answers the
          question.

GS-33.   Write an equation, then find the missing length in each diagram.

          a)   b)

GS-34.   Sourdough Sam's wife, Ann, thought about visiting one of her quilting friends on her way
          home from town. To do so, she would have to travel 24 km south to her friend's house and
          then 32 km west to her home. Instead, she decided to go straight home. What is the
          distance directly to her home? Write and solve an equation to find the distance.

GS-35.   The hypotenuse and one leg of a right triangle are 65 and 60 meters.

          a)   What is the length of the third side?

          b)   Find the area and the perimeter of the triangle.

GS-36. Rosie and Josie are sisters from Ann's quilting club with a problem similar to that of Luke and Duke. They will be sharing the square plots of land around a lake (shown at right). Rosie will get the two square plots of land on the shorter sides, and Josie will get the square plot of land on the longer side.

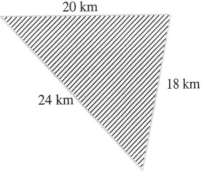

20 km

18 km

24 km

a) Find the area of Josie's piece. Find the area of Rosie's pieces combined.

b) Is this a fair share? Why or why not?

c) What is different between Luke and Duke's lakes and Rosie and Josie's?

GS-37. Compute each value.

a) 6^5

b) 4^7

c) 1.5^3

d) 0.04^2

e) $(2 + 3)^4$

f) $2(3 + 4)^3$

GS-38. Samantha, the owner of Noble Ranch, must pay taxes on her land. She calculated the acreage as 5920 acres. The tax rate is four cents per acre. The government has sent her a bill showing that she owes $281.60 in taxes. Help Sam decide if her tax bill is accurate.

a) Calculate Samantha's tax bill.

b) What conclusions can you make about Samantha's tax bill? Include the amount of tax Samantha should pay in your explanation.

GS-39. Nestor, a local farmer, also received a tax bill for his homestead. The tax rate is $25.60 per square mile or four cents per acre. His taxes amount to $15.60. Use the diagram at right and the questions below to find the area of Nestor's farm. Decide if his tax bill is accurate.

0.5 mi   A   B
0.5 mi   0.6 mi

a) What is the area of Nestor's farm in square miles? Show all subproblems.

b) What is the area of Nestor's farm in acres? A square mile is equal to 640 acres.

c) Compute Nestor's tax bill. Is his tax bill accurate? Explain.

GS-40.   Follow your teacher's directions for practicing mental math.

GS-41.   Obtain a resource page from your teacher for the next two problems. Find the length of
   the line segment below right by completing parts (a) through (c).

a)   Draw a right triangle with the line segment
      shown at right as the hypotenuse.

b)   How many units long are the legs?

c)   Use an equation to find the length of the line
      segment (hypotenuse).

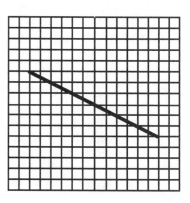

Find the lengths of each of the following segments. Be sure to show all your work.

d)   e)

GS-42.   The Claude-Hopper family has decided to build pens for
          their animals. To keep the different animals separated
          from each other, they need to build four pens. The pigs
          are to be kept in a square pen with a side length of 15
          feet. The mule pen will also be square and will measure
          36 feet on each side. The third square pen is for the
          oxen. In the middle is a right triangular pen for the
          chickens. Find the total area of the four pens.

a)   Copy and label the drawing of each animal pen.

b)   The calculation of the area of each pen is a
      subproblem that helps answer the question.

>>Problem continues on the next page.>>

Solve each of the five subproblems.

i)   What is the area of pig pen?

ii) What is the area of the mule pen?

iii) What is the hypotenuse of the chicken pen?

iv) What is the area of the chicken pen?

v)   What is the area of the oxen pen?

c)   Use your answers from part (b) to find the total area of the farm pens.

S-43.   Use subproblems to solve the problem below. Copy and label the drawing. List the subproblems, then solve each one.

Regal Ranch has four agricultural sectors: Sectors A and B are rectangles; sectors C and D are right triangles. Measurements are shown in miles.

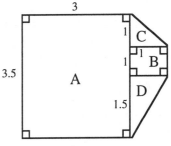

a)   What is the total area of the ranch in square miles? Show the subproblems you use.

b)   One square mile is equal to 640 acres. How many acres is Regal Ranch?

S-44.   Clem and Clyde set up a tent at the base of Lookout Peak. They pounded a stake in the ground five feet from the center pole so they could attach a rope to it. If the rope they attached to the very top of the center pole was 13 feet long, how tall was the center pole? Draw and label a diagram. Show all your work as you solve this problem.

GS-45.

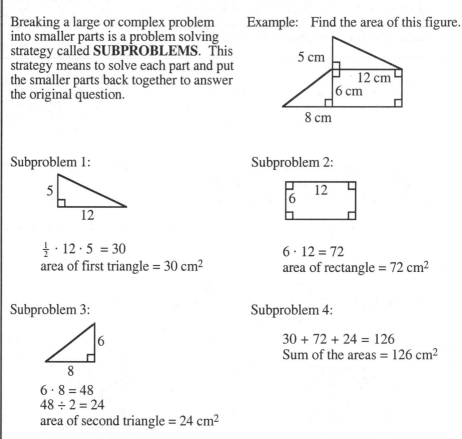

SUBPROBLEMS

Breaking a large or complex problem into smaller parts is a problem solving strategy called **SUBPROBLEMS**. This strategy means to solve each part and put the smaller parts back together to answer the original question.

Example: Find the area of this figure.

5 cm
12 cm
6 cm
8 cm

Subproblem 1:

5
12

$\frac{1}{2} \cdot 12 \cdot 5 = 30$
area of first triangle = 30 cm^2

Subproblem 2:

6   12

$6 \cdot 12 = 72$
area of rectangle = 72 cm^2

Subproblem 3:

6
8

$6 \cdot 8 = 48$
$48 \div 2 = 24$
area of second triangle = 24 cm^2

Subproblem 4:

$30 + 72 + 24 = 126$
Sum of the areas = 126 cm^2

Make these notes in your Tool Kit the to right of the double-lined box.

Draw a figure that would need to be broken into smaller parts to find its area. Write the subproblems you would have to solve.

GS-46.   Clem and Clyde staked out a claim for land just outside Bovine Gulch. The boundaries form a square, a rectangle, and a right triangle. Find the total area of their land in square miles and tell them how much fencing they need to fence the outside of their land.

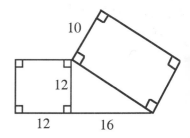

10
12
12   16

GS-47.   Jo Jo plays third base and Dano plays first base on the
          Stickball Cactus League team. Jo Jo is standing at
          third base and throws the ball to Dano. How far apart
          are the bases? Draw a picture to help you. The
          distance between each base is 90 feet.

GS-48.   Find the total area of the rectangle and
          right triangle combination shown at right.
          Be sure to show all your subproblems.

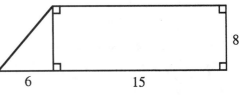

8

6   15

GS-49.   Find the lengths of each of the following segments. Be sure to show all your work.

a)   b)

GS-50.   A right triangle has a base of 15 cm and an area of
          90 cm². Find its perimeter. Show all your
          subproblems.

15 cm

GS-51.   The figure shown at right is made up of a right triangle and a rectangle.

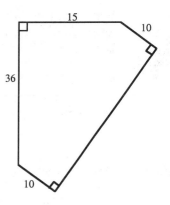

a)   Draw a line to help divide the figure into two subproblems.

b)   Use the dimensions given to find the area of the triangle, the rectangle, and the whole figure. Be sure to show all your subproblems.

GS-52.   Plot the points P(0, 0) and T(4, 4) on a square grid.

a)   Find all the squares that have P and T as two of the four vertices.

b)   Find the sum of the areas of these squares.

GS-53.   Try to make a square out of 20 tiles. Is it possible?

a)   What is the area of the largest square you can make with 20 tiles? What are the lengths of its sides?

b)   How many more tiles would you need to make the next biggest square? What is th area of this square? What would be the lengths of its sides?

c)   Why does it make sense that $\sqrt{20}$ is between 4 and 5?

d)   Do you think $\sqrt{20}$ is closer to 4 or to 5? Explain your reasoning.

GS-54.   The area of a square is 60 square units, so the length of the side is not a whole number.

a)   Between which two whole numbers is the side length?

b)   Between which two whole numbers is the side length of a square that has an area of 32?

c)   Between which two whole numbers is the side length of a square that has an area of 8?

GS-55. Between which two whole numbers is each of the following square roots? To which whole number do you think it is closer? (For example: $\sqrt{125}$ is between 11 and 12 and is closer to 11.)

a) $\sqrt{40}$ b) $\sqrt{95}$ c) $\sqrt{3}$ d) $\sqrt{200}$

e) $\sqrt{59}$ f) $\sqrt{75.5}$ g) $\sqrt{154}$ h) $\sqrt{320}$

GS-56. Describe your method for estimating the approximate value of a square root when the number is not a perfect square.

GS-57. Spencer and Reba were comparing their answers from an earlier problem. They agreed that $\sqrt{40}$ was between 6 and 7. Spencer said, "I think $\sqrt{40}$ is about 6.5, since 40 is about halfway between 36 and 49." Reba's estimate of $\sqrt{40}$ was $6\frac{4}{13}$. Spencer was astonished. "How on earth did you come up with *that* number?"

"Easy," replied Reba. "I just looked at the patterns in the building squares problem GS-20. I know that 40 tiles is 4 more than 36, and 36 is the perfect square of $6 \cdot 6$. I also know that I need 13 more tiles to get from 36 to 49, and 49 is the perfect square of $7 \cdot 7$. I figured that 40 tiles is enough for a square that is 6 by 6, and I have **4** out of the **13** tiles that I need for a square that is $7 \cdot 7$. It makes sense to me that a good estimate of $\sqrt{40}$ is $6\frac{4}{13}$. What do you think, Spencer?" Spencer was not so sure. He wanted to check the value on a calculator.

a) Use your calculator to make a decimal approximation of $\sqrt{40}$. Round your answer to the nearest hundredth (0.01).

b) How close to your answer from part (a) is Spencer's estimate of 6.5?

c) Convert Reba's estimate of $6\frac{4}{13}$ to a decimal. How close is Reba's estimate?

GS-58. Use Reba's method to approximate the following square roots. Copy and complete the table. Express your answer as a mixed number, then compare your mixed number with a calculator approximation.

	$\sqrt{45}$	$\sqrt{50}$	$\sqrt{91}$	$\sqrt{110}$	$\sqrt{150}$	$\sqrt{15}$
Mixed Number						
Converted to a Decimal						
Calculated to the Nearest 0.01						

GS-59. Find the total area and perimeter of the figure at right. Be sure to show all of your subproblems.

GS-60. Jon invested $500 at 3.8% compound interest per year. How much money will he have at the end of six years?

GS-61. Find the length of the missing side of each of these right triangles.

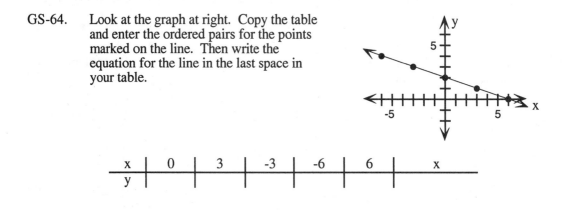

a)

b)

c)

GS-62. Solve these equations for x. Check your answers.

a) $(x + 4.5)2 = 32$ b) $6 + 2.5x = 21$ c) $3x + 8.4 = 19.2$

GS-63. Sara finds a sweater for $49.99. If she has $54 and sales tax is 8%, does she have enough money to buy the sweater?

GS-64. Look at the graph at right. Copy the table and enter the ordered pairs for the points marked on the line. Then write the equation for the line in the last space in your table.

x	0	3	-3	-6	6	x
y						

GS-65. Follow your teacher's directions for practicing mental math.

GS-66.   Your teacher will give you two resource pages per study team. Each member of your
          study team will cut out one figure, fold it along the bold lines and tape it together. Put all
          four three-dimensional objects where all members of the team can examine them.

   a)   How many faces do your prisms have, excluding the top and bottom (shaded faces)?

   b)   Describe the faces of your prism.

   c)   What do you notice about the bases (top and bottom) of the prisms?

   d)   Describe the shaded bases (top and bottom) of the prisms your team made.
         What are their shapes?

   e)   Prisms are named by the shape of their bases. List the names of the prisms.

GS-67.

PRISMS

A **PRISM** is a three-dimensional figure composed
of polygonal faces (called sides or lateral sides) and
two congruent, parallel faces called bases. No holes
are permitted in the solid. The remaining faces are
parallelograms (or other special quadrilaterals). A
prism is named for the shape of its base.

          Your study team built models of four different prisms. Since you will need to refer to
          these prisms to help you solve future problems, you will now make your own set of the
          prisms to place in your Tool Kit. Rather than taping the edges together to form solid
          models, you should leave them untaped so they can lay flat for storage and be "popped
          up" when the model is needed.

          Cut out each of the four prisms from the resource pages you received from your teacher.
          Fold and unfold along the bold-faced lines, then attach one base of each prism to your
          Tool Kit page with tape (or glue).

In your Tool Kit to the right of
each model sketch each of its
faces.

GS-68.   Sam put $1000 worth of gold in a savings account. He will earn 3.5% compound interest
          per year. How much money will he have in three years?

GS-69.   Carol went on another shopping spree. She bought a pair of $65 jeans at 40% off, a $2[cut off]
          tank top at $\frac{1}{4}$ off, and a pair of $35 shoes at 30% off. How much did she save? How
          much did she pay for all three items?

GS-70.   In 1997 a box of 300 glass marbles sold at Ronna's
          auction house for £2760. At the time, £1 (British
          pound) was worth $1.57. What did the box of
          marbles sell for in U.S. dollars?

GS-71.   Find the length of the missing side.

          a)   b)

GS-72.   Solve for x.

          a) $\frac{1}{2} = \frac{5x}{10}$ b) $\frac{3x}{9} = \frac{x+2}{6}$ c) $\frac{x+2}{5} = \frac{2x+1}{3}$

GS-73.   Find each of the following.

          a) $|-15| + |-26|$ b) $-|-40|$ c) $|0.5| + |-1\frac{1}{2}|$ d) $|24| + |-15|$

GS-74.   The diameter of the large circle is 18 cm.

          a) What is the area of the shaded circle?

          b) What subproblems did you do to find the answer?

S-75. Look at this drawing of a box, which is also called a rectangular prism. It is one inch high (thick).

1 in.

3 in.   4 in.

a) If you had several one cubic inch blocks (1" x 1" x 1"), how many blocks would you need to completely fill the rectangular prism?

b) What is another name for the number of blocks needed to fill the prism?

c) What kinds of units are used to label volume?

S-76. We have added layers to the prism from the previous problem.

5 in.

3 in.   4 in.

a) How many layers have been added? How many total layers are in this prism?

b) Let h stand for the height of the prism. What is the value of h?

c) What are the dimensions of the base in this figure?

d) Let A stand for the <u>area</u> of the base. What is the value of A?

e) In the previous problem you calculated that it would take 12 blocks to fill the prism when it was 1 layer high. Now that it is 5 layers high, how many blocks do you think it will take to fill it completely? Explain how you arrived at your answer.

f) Using V for volume, h for height (number of layers), and A for the area of the base, write a formula for finding the volume of a prism.

S-77. Examine the prism at right.

3

2   3

a) What is the area of the base (A)?

b) What is the height (h)?

c) Calculate the volume of this prism.

GS-78. The figure at right is a triangular prism.

a) Find the area of its base.

b) Find its volume.

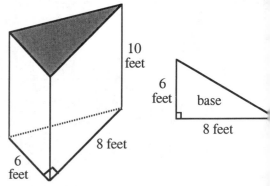

10 feet

6 feet | base

8 feet

8 feet

6 feet

GS-79.

VOLUME OF A PRISM

The **VOLUME** of a prism is the area of either base (A) times the height (h) of the prism.

$$V = (\textbf{Area of base}) \cdot (\textbf{height})$$

$$V = Ah$$

Example:

Area of base = (2 in.)(3 in.) = 6 in.^{2}

(Area of base)(height) = (6 in.^{2})(4 in.) = 24 in.^{3}

Volume = 24 in.^{3}

4 in.

2 in.   3 in.

Describe how to find the area of the base for a triangular prism in your Tool Kit to the right of the double-lined box.

GS-80. The height of a prism whose base is shown at right is 35 units.

a) Find the area of the base of the figure.

b) What is the volume of the prism? Show your work.

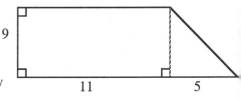

9

11   5

GS-81.   Find the length of each of the following segments. Be sure to show all your work.

a)   b)

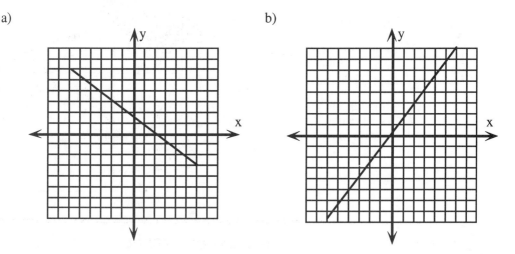

GS-82.   Delbert's parents said he watches too much television on the weekends. He wanted to
          show them that he watches about the same amount as his peers. Delbert collected
          information from ten students about how much time they spend watching television.
          From one weekend, the students reported viewing times of 240, 0, 60, 30, 120, 900, 65, 90,
          240, and 195 minutes.

a)   Find the mean, median, and mode of these times.

b)   Suppose the student who reported 900 minutes had not come to school, so Delbert
      only had the other nine reported times. Compute the new mean, median, and mode.

c)   Which of the measures of central tendency is most useful for Delbert to convince his
      parents he is not watching too much television?

GS-83.   Listed below are sets of leg lengths for triangles. Determine if each set of dimensions
          would result in a right triangle.

a)   42   144   150   b)   45   108   117

c)   7   19   25   d)   56   216   225

GS-84.   A bag contains 11 red, 5 yellow, and 7 purple marbles. Find the probability of drawing a
          purple marble followed by a red marble. The purple marble was not put back in the bag.

GS-85. Examine the figure at right.

a) Find the area of the figure. List all your subproblems and show your work.

b) If the figure represents the base of a prism of height 7 inches, what is its volume?

GS-86. Take out your Tool Kit and turn to your entry on prisms. Use the dimensions on your rectangular prism (4 by 6 by 20) to answer the following questions.

a) Find the area of the shaded top (base).

b) Find the area of the shaded bottom (base).

c) Find the areas of each of the lateral faces.

d) Find the sum of the areas of all of the faces and bases.

e) Why do you think this number is called the **surface area** of this rectangular prisr

GS-87. Now you will calculate the surface area of the other three pop-up prisms. Refer to problem GS-86 for the subproblems and to the pop-ups in your Tool Kit. All dimensi are in centimeters. The bases of the pop-up prisms are:

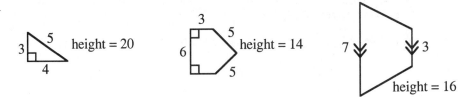

a) What is the surface area of the triangular prism?

b) What is the surface area of the pentagonal prism?

c) What is the surface area of the trapezoidal prism?

CHAPTER

GS-88.   The base of your prism can be used to find its volume.

a)   Calculate the base area of each prism.

b)   What is the height of each prism?

c)   What is the total volume of each prism? Be sure to label the volume in cubic units.

d)   Explain how you calculated the volume of each prism.

GS-89.   Consider the drawing at right. All the angles are right angles.

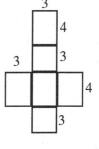

a)   Imagine folding along the bold lines. Sketch the prism it would cover. Which of your pop-up models could represent this prism?

b)   What would be the dimensions (length, width, and height) of the prism?

c)   What is the volume?

d)   Find the area of all of the faces, including the bases. List the subproblems used to find these areas.

e)   What is the total surface area (the sum of all of the faces and bases)?

GS-90.

SURFACE AREA OF A PRISM

The **SURFACE AREA** of a prism is the sum of the areas of all of the faces, including the bases. Surface area is expressed in **square units**.

Example: Find the surface area of the triangular prism at right.

Subproblem 1: Area of the 2 bases

$$2\left[\tfrac{1}{2}(6 \text{ cm})(8 \text{ cm})\right] = 48 \text{ cm}^2$$

Subproblem 2: Area of the 3 sides (lateral faces)

Area of side 1: (6 cm)(7 cm) = 42 cm²
Area of side 2: (8 cm)(7 cm) = 56 cm²
Area of side 3: (10 cm)(7 cm) = 70 cm²

Subproblem 3: Surface Area of Prism = sum of bases and lateral faces

$$48 \text{ cm}^2 + 42 \text{ cm}^2 + 56 \text{ cm}^2 + 70 \text{ cm}^2 = 216 \text{ cm}^2$$

>>Problem continues on the next page.>>

Make these notes in your Tool Kit to the right of the double-lined box.

a)   Why is surface area expressed in square units?

b)   In your own words describe what "surface area" means.

GS-91.   Find the surface area of a rectangular prism with a base of six feet by five feet and a height of seven feet. Use your pop-up model as a guide. List the subproblems needed to solve this problem.

GS-92.   Miss Lilly rode the stagecoach to Bovine Gulch. When the stage arrived, she discovered that her trunk of valuable quilt fabrics had fallen off the stage. If the trunk was a rectangular prism that measured 2 feet by 3 feet by 1.5 feet, what was its volume?

GS-93.   The drawing shown at right represents the piece of brown paper Miss Lilly used to wrap Clem and Clyde's present. All angles are right angles.

a)   Draw a sketch of the box that can be wrapped in this paper without any waste or overlap. Label its dimensions.

b)   Find the surface area of the box.

c)   Find the volume of the box.

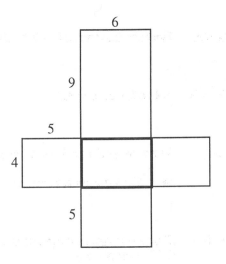

GS-94.   Find the area and perimeter of the figure shown at right. List each subproblem and show your work.

CHAPTER 8

GS-95. Describe how to find the third side of a right triangle if you know the length of:

a) the hypotenuse and one leg.

b) both of the legs.

GS-96. Find the volume of the prism with the base shown at right and a height of 8. List the subproblems before you begin.

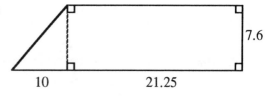

10   21.25   7.6

GS-97. Solve the following equations for x. Check your solution.

a) 6x + 8 = x − 12

b) 1000 = -20x + 400

c) -6x − 1 = 125

d) $\frac{x - 11}{25} = \frac{24}{30}$

GS-98. Solve 2r = d for r.

GS-99. Find the diameter of a circle if the radius is 7.58 centimeters.

GS-100. Solve for d: C = πd.

GS-101. The radius of a circle is 6.5 centimeters.

a) Find the circumference.

b) Find the area.

GS-102. Find the volume of a prism that has a base area of 20.3 square centimeters and a height of 17.75 centimeters.

GS-103. Make a sketch of the two paper cylinders shown at right. Label the height of each one and write, "I think this one will have more volume" under the cylinder you believe will have more volume.

11"

8.5"

GS-104. Examine the cylinders above right. Each cylinder has been constructed from a piece of paper that measures $8\frac{1}{2}$ inches by 11 inches.

a) In your notebook, make a sketch of the <u>base</u> of the tall cylinder and label the circumference. Write under the lateral area its sketch for each.

b) Calculate the diameter and the radius of the tall cylinder. Add these measurements to your sketch. Find the area of the base. Show your work.

c) Make a sketch of the base of the short cylinder and label the circumference. Fill in the lateral area.

d) Calculate the diameter and the radius. Add these measurements to your sketch, then find the area of the base. Show your work.

GS-105. Refer to the diagram of the cylinders in problem GS-103. Imagine that you cut one inch off the bottom of the <u>tall</u> cylinder so that you now have a new cylinder with the same base that is exactly one inch tall.

a) Make a sketch of this cylinder.

b) How many one-inch squares would it take to cover the <u>base</u> of this cylinder?

c) If you had one-inch cubes, how many cubes would it take to <u>fill</u> this cylinder?

d) What do you notice about your answers to parts (b) and (c)? Explain your observation.

e) Can you use the information from parts (b) through (d) to find how many cubes it would take to fill the original <u>tall</u> cylinder? Explain your method.

GS-106. Imagine that you cut one inch off the bottom of the <u>short</u> cylinder so that you now have a new cylinder (with the same base) that is exactly one inch tall.

a) Make a sketch of this cylinder.

b) Use the process in parts (b) through (e) of the previous problem to find the volume of the original short cylinder.

GS-107. Ann and Nan were writing formulas for finding the volume of a cylinder. Ann wrote, "V = Ah." Nan wrote, "V = πr²h." Their math teacher examined their work and announced that they were both correct.

a) Compare the two formulas. What do variables V, A, and h represent? What does πr^2 represent?

b) Explain why Ann and Nan are both correct.

c) Express A in terms of πr^2 in the first formula.

GS-108.

VOLUME OF A CYLINDER

The **VOLUME OF A CYLINDER** is found by multiplying the base area (A) times the height (h).

Volume = (Area of base)(height)
$$V = Ah = (\pi r^2)(h)$$

Example:

Find the volume of the cylinder at right.

$A = \pi(12)^2 = 144\pi$
$V = 144\pi(15) = 2160\pi \approx 6785.84$ cm³

12 cm

15 cm

Look at the example in the Tool Kit. To the right of the double-lined box, explain why the answer is given as cm³.

GS-109. Draw a diagram and find the volume of a cylinder that has a radius of 15.3 centimeters and a height of 12 centimeters.

GS-110. Answer these questions and show your work.

r = 5 cm

10 cm

a) What is the area of the base of the cylinder above right?

b) What is the volume of that cylinder?

c) Find the area of the base of the cylinder below right.

d) Find the volume of that cylinder.

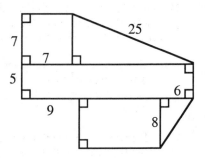

r = 3.4 cm

9 cm

GS-111. Use the figure at right.

a) Find the total area. Be sure to show all your subproblems.

b) If the figure is the base of a prism with a height of 14, find the volume.

7

25

7

5

9

6

8

GS-112. Find each of the following.

a) $-|-93|$ b) $|-20| + |63|$ c) $|-\frac{1}{2}| - |-\frac{1}{2}|$ d) $|102| - |97|$

GS-113. Write and solve a proportion for the following problem.

In a recent survey for the student council, Dominique found that 150 students out of a total of 800 students on campus did <u>not</u> like soda. If half of the student body was going to attend a dance, how many students could she expect would want soda?

GS-114. Jian has two large bags of candies: the first one has 100 red jellybeans and 300 black jellybeans; the second one has 200 red jellybeans, 100 black jellybeans, and 300 green jellybeans. He grabs a bag at random, reaches into it and pulls out one jellybean.

a) What is the probability that it is green?

b) What is the probability that it is red?

GS-115.   Find the area of a rectangle with the given dimensions.

a)   base = $4\frac{1}{2}$ mm, height = $1\frac{1}{5}$ mm   b)   base = 1.26 m, height = 5.6 m

GS-116.   Find the area of a circle with the given dimension.

a)   radius = 1.3 cm   b)   diameter = 5.5 m

GS-117.   Find the circumference of a circle with the given dimension.

a)   radius = 7.3 cm   b)   diameter = 8.5 m

GS-118.   Below is the net of a cylinder. Find the total surface area (the area of the three separate pieces added together) of the cylinder's net. (A **net** is a two-dimensional unfolded picture of a three-dimensional object.)

a)   The height of the cylinder is 7.2 cm. The longer side of the rectangle is the same measurement as what part of the circle?

b)   Show the subproblems you used to find the total area of this cylinder (that is, the surface area of all three pieces).

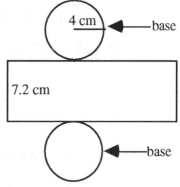

GS-119.   Use the net at right to answer the questions below. It is not drawn to scale.

a)   What is the circumference of the base of this cylinder?

b)   Use your answer to part (a) to find the radius of the base.

c)   Find the total surface area of this cylinder.

GS-120.   Which of the cylinders matches the net?

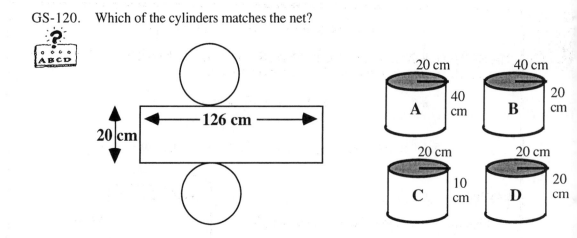

GS-121.   Find the surface area of a soda can with a radius of 5 centimeters and a height of 18 centimeters. Sketch and show your work. List the subproblems you used.

GS-122.   Explain in your own words how to find the surface area of a cylinder.

SURFACE AREA OF A CYLINDER

The **SURFACE AREA OF A CYLINDER** is the sum of the two base areas and the lateral surface area. The formula for the surface area is:

$$\text{S.A.} = 2\pi r^2 + \pi dh$$
$$= 2\pi r^2 + 2\pi rh$$

where r = radius, d = diameter, and h = height of the cylinder.

Example:

Find the surface area of the cylinder at right.

28 cm

25 cm

Subproblem 1:   Area of the two circular bases

$2[\pi(28\text{ cm})^2] = 1568\pi\text{ cm}^2$

Subproblem 2:   Area of the lateral face

$\pi(56)25 = 1400\pi\text{ cm}^2$

Subproblem 3:   Surface area of the cylinder

$1568\pi\text{ cm}^2 + 1400\pi\text{ cm}^2 = 2968\pi\text{ cm}^2$
$\approx 9324.25\text{ cm}^2$

rectangle

circumference of base

25 cm

Make these notes in your Tool Kit to the right of the double-lined box.

a)   How is finding the surface area of a cylinder different than finding the surface area of a prism?

b)   How is it the same?

GS-124.   Find the diameters of the following circles. Show your work.

a)   A circle with a circumference of 31.40 cm.

b)   A circle with an area of 56.5 square inches.

c)   A circle with a radius of 8.16 meters.

GS-125. The figure at right represents the base of a prism with a height of 12.

a)   Find the area of the base. Show all subproblems.

b)   Find the volume of the prism.

GS-126. Luke Wrangler added a rectangular gate to the fence he built around his homestead. The gate was 6 feet high and was reinforced with a 10-foot diagonal board.

a)   Draw a diagram of the gate and the diagonal. Be sure to label your drawing.

b)   Find the width of the gate.

GS-127. Archimedes the Arachnid was a spider who so admired his namesake, the great Greek mathematician, that he made all his webs very geometric. One day, he made a web like the one below right by going 1 centimeter from his starting point S to point A, spinning a strand, making a 90° turn, going one more centimeter (to B), and then going back to his starting point (S). Then he went along the web back to B, made a 90° turn, and spun webs one more centimeter (to C), and then back to S. He kept doing this until he had spun a 6-centimeter strand on his <u>return</u> to point S. How many strands did he spin? Note that a strand is the distance between two points. The problem asks <u>how many strands</u>, not the sum of their lengths.

GS-128. **The Mine Shaft**

Sourdough Sam was given a gold mine. To get the gold, Sourdough Sam's mining company will build a sturdy entry platform for the new mine shaft. The platform will be a rectangular prism 4 feet high with a base 20 feet by 15 feet. The concrete for the platform will be poured around a cylindrical hole 6 feet in diameter. The miners will be lowered through the hole to get to the vein of gold. Sam needs to know how many cubic feet of concrete to order and how much it will weigh.

a) How many cubic feet of concrete will be needed to build the platform?

b) If concrete weighs 120 pounds per cubic foot, how much will the platform weigh?

c) If each donkey cart can haul 350 pounds of concrete, how many cart loads will be needed?

d) If the entire platform including the center hole (but not the bottom) is painted, what area will the paint cover?

GS-129. **Chapter Summary**

Like many other gold miners' wives, Sourdough Sam's wife, Ann, spends many evenings quilting while Sam is at the mine. You will help her with her most recent project. Take the colored paper your teacher provides and create an individual summary quilt piece. Choose one of the main ideas of this chapter and a representative problem. As you have done in other chapters, write a clear explanation of your solution. You must include a picture or diagram.

GS-130. Find the length of the missing side in each triangle below.

a)

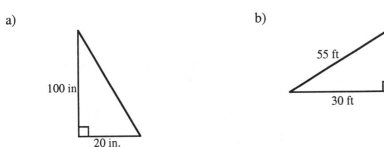

b)

GS-131. This figure represents the base of a prism with a height of 6.

a) Find the area of the base. Show all subproblems.

b) Find the volume of this prism.

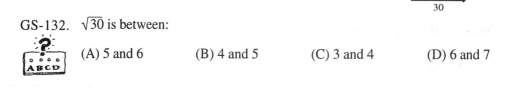

GS-132. $\sqrt{30}$ is between:

(A) 5 and 6   (B) 4 and 5   (C) 3 and 4   (D) 6 and 7

GS-133. Mrs. Wrangler is planning a birthday party for her grandson, Arnold, at the Bar K Ran It costs $75 for up to 12 children and $8.50 for each additional child. Arnold wants to invite 15 friends. How much will Mrs. Wrangler have to pay for Arnold's party?

GS-134. The horse trough at Sam's mine looked very much like a rectangular prism with no top. It measured eight feet long by three feet wide by two feet deep. It had recently rained, the trough was completely full. How much water was in the horse trough?

GS-135. The figure at right is a barn at the Wrangler Ranch. Use the following information and the dimensions shown on the drawing to find the surface area of the barn so that Luke and Duke will know how much whitewash to buy. It is 28 feet from the ground to the top of the roof. They will not whitewash the door, window, floor, or roof. List the subproblems needed to find the total area to be whitewashed.

GS-136. The Wranglers built a barn, a storage shed, and a house. The storage shed was 70 pace due east from the house. The barn was 240 paces due south of the storage shed. How many paces is it from the barn to the house? Draw and label a diagram and show all subproblems.

GS-137. Find the volume of the cylinder at right. Explain the steps that you followed.

7 cm

14 cm

GS-138. Solve the following equations.

a) $x = \dfrac{4}{5} \div \dfrac{1}{2}$

b) $x = 6 \div \dfrac{7}{8}$

GS-139. **What We Have Done in This Chapter**

Below is a list of the Tool Kit entries from this chapter.

- GS-2   Right Triangles
- GS-8   Measurement in Different Dimensions
- GS-9   Pythagorean Theorem
- GS-24   Squaring and Square Root
- GS-26   Bases and Exponents
- GS-45   Subproblems
- GS-67   Prisms
- GS-79   Volume of a Prism
- GS-90   Surface Area of a Prism
- GS-108   Volume of a Cylinder
- GS-123   Surface Area of a Cylinder

Review all the entries and read the notes you made in your Tool Kit. Make a list of any questions, terms, or notes you do not understand. Ask your partner or study team members for help. If anything is still unclear, ask your teacher.

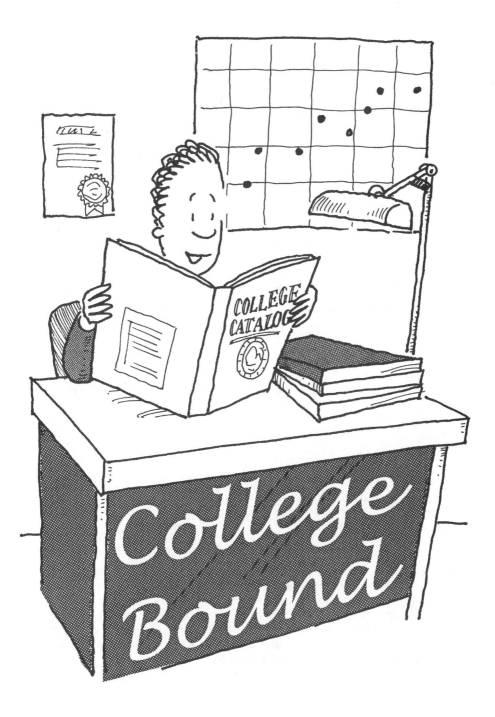

Chapter 9

Chapter 9
College Bound: SLOPES AND RATES OF CHANGE

In this chapter you will extend your knowledge of data tables, writing equations, and graphing. As you work on this chapter, you will see that many mathematical ideas are intertwined. You will be able to describe and identify linear graphs from their equations or data tables and write linear equations from linear graphs or data tables. You will apply these skills in problem solving contexts and real-life situations.

In this chapter you will have the opportunity to:

- find the rate of change of a set of data.

- use slope triangles to find the rate of change of a line.

- write equations from graphs and data tables.

- graph lines using the slope and the y-intercept.

- graph and solve inequalities.

Read the problem below, but **do not try to solve it now**. What you learn over the next few days will enable you to solve it.

CB-0.   George and Ben are two friends who make extra money parking cars at concerts and sporting events at the big arena near their homes in Indianapolis. They both want to go to college to become architects. Ben wants to go to Indiana-Purdue University at Fort Wayne, but George wants to start at the local community college and transfer in two years. Both are worried about the expense of college since neither of their families can afford to help. Use the information provided to decide if the boys will earn enough to be able to attend college.

Number Sense

Algebra and Functions

Mathematical Reasoning

Measurement and Geometry

Statistics, Data Analysis, & Probability

Chapter 9
College Bound: SLOPES AND RATES OF CHANGE

CB-1.   Complete the table and write the rule.

x	-1	0	1	2	3	4	5	x
y	4	1	-2	-5				

a)   How can you tell from the table if the graph is a line or a curve?

b)   Graph the data.

c)   Describe the direction of the graph as it goes from left to right.

CB-2.   **Cash on Hand (Part One)**

Kristie, Samantha, Connie, and Julie are four
friends who work part-time in one of the
concession stands at the arena. One Saturday,
each girl earned $15. Over the next week:

a)   Kristie saves an additional $2.50 per day.

b)   Samantha saves an additional $1.50 per day.

c)   Connie spends $2 per day.

d)   Julie neither spends any of her money nor saves any additional money.

Construct a table like the one below or use the resource page provided by your teacher to
show the changes for each girl's cash on hand over the next seven days. Let the x-value
represent the days and let the y-value represent the cash on hand. Use the table below to
help get you started. Day 0 is Saturday.

Day (x)	0	1	2	3	4	5	6	7	x
Kristie	$15								
Samantha	$15								
Connie	$15								
Julie	$15								

e)   How much money will Kristie, Samantha, Connie, and Julie each have on the
following Saturday (the seventh day)?

f)   Write an equation for each girl's situation that shows how much money she will
have on any given day.

CB-3.   **Cash on Hand (Part Two)**

On the resource page your teacher gives you, create a graph to compare the girls' financ situations by following the directions below.

a)   On the same set of axes, graph the cash on hand for Kristie, Samantha, Connie, ar Julie. Use a different color for each girl's graph. Label each graph with the name of the girl and the equation.

b)   What is similar about the four graphs?

c)   Compare the graphs of Kristie and Samantha. How are they alike? Describe the direction of the graph for both girls. How are the graphs different?

d)   Now compare Connie's graph to Kristie's and Samantha's graphs. Describe wh; you see.

e)   Compare Julie's graph with the others. Describe what you see.

CB-4.   **Cash on Hand (Part Three)**

The girls have another friend, Maleya. Maleya does not work with them at the concessi stand and did not earn any money that day. However, she has been able to save $2.50 from baby-sitting each day since Sunday.

a)   Construct a table or use the resource page provided by your teacher for Maleya, th add her data to the graph you made for the other girls. Remember to label the line with her name and equation.

b)   Compare Maleya's graph to Kristie's graph. Will Maleya and Kristie ever have t same amount of money at the same time? Explain your answer.

c)   When will Maleya have more money than Connie? When will she have more money than Julie?

d)   Will Maleya ever have more money than Samantha? How can you tell?

CB-5.   Use the graph shown below to answer the following questions.

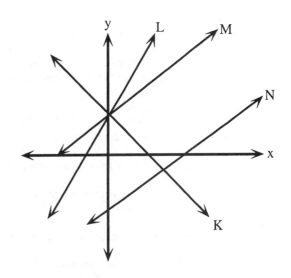

a)   Compare and contrast lines L, M, N, and K. Be as detailed as possible.

b)   Which line appears steepest?

c)   Which lines appear to have the same steepness?

d)   How is line K different from the other lines?

CB-6.

DESCRIBING LINES

Lines are described by their steepness and direction as they are viewed from <u>left to right</u>. Lines that go up show a positive rate of change. Lines that go down show a negative rate of change.

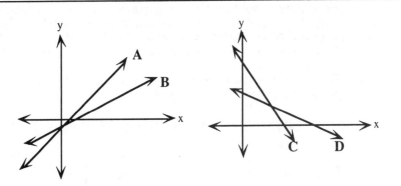

a)   Copy the graphs above.

b)   Compare the steepness of lines A and B, C and D, then A and C.

c)   Describe the direction of these lines. Which lines go up? Which go down?

CB-7. Lucy is a vendor selling boxes of popcorn at the arena. The table at right shows how many boxes of popcorn she sells throughout the day.

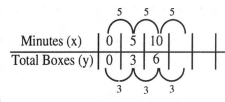

Minutes (x)	0	5	10		
Total Boxes (y)	0	3	6		

a) Assuming she continues to sell popcorn at this rate, copy and complete the table at right.

b) What pattern do you see in the table?

c) At what rate is she selling popcorn? Express your answer in boxes per minute.

d) How many boxes of popcorn will she sell in one hour?

CB-8. Find the area and perimeter of the triangle at right.

7 km   4 km   12 km   10 km

CB-9. On a radio show Polly won a $250 gift certificate to a local health club. The cost to become a member is $99, and the monthly membership fee is $16.50. How long can Polly use the health club before she runs out of money from her gift certificate? Write an equation and solve it.

CB-10. Solve for x.

a) $\frac{1}{2}x - 3 = -7$

b) $\frac{1}{2}x + \frac{1}{4} = 3$

c) $\frac{5}{8}x + \frac{2}{3} = 1\frac{11}{12}$

d) $\frac{x}{3} = \frac{21}{7}$

CB-11. Complete the following Diamond Problems.

Product
Sum
a)   b)   c)   d)

B-12.   Now that we have started a new chapter, it is time for you to organize your binder.

   a)   Put the work from the last chapter in order and keep it in a separate folder.

   b)   When this is completed, write, "I have organized my binder."

B-13.   Mr. Drawsalot is the landscape architect for the new museum near the local sports arena. He was asked to draw a picture of what the front of the building would look like five years after its completion. A row of trees will be planted along the front of the building. The trees will be three feet tall when planted, and in his drawing the trees will be 13 feet tall.

   a)   Assuming the trees will grow the same amount each year, copy and complete the table below. Let $x = 0$ be the year the trees are planted.

Year (x)	0	1	2	3	4	5	x
Height (y)	3					13	

   b)   Graph the information from your table and label it with its equation. Make sure you are careful and accurate. You will use your graph again later in the chapter.

   c)   What is the change in <u>time</u> from one x-value to the next?

   d)   What is the change in <u>height</u> from one y-value to the next?

   e)   What ratio describes the growth rate of the trees? Write this **rate of change** as a ratio with units.

   f)   What part of the equation shows the rate of change?

   g)   Analyze your data table as shown below. Mark the rate of change across the table.

$$\text{rate of change} = \frac{\text{change in height}}{\text{change in time}}$$

Year (x)	0	1	2	3	4	5	x
Height (y)	3	5	7	9	11	13	2x + 3

(+1 +1 marked above Year; +2 +2 marked below Height)

3-14.   Continue using your marked data table to answer the following questions.

   a)   Add year 10 and year 20 to your data table.

   b)   What is the change in <u>time</u> from year 5 to year 10? What is the change in <u>height</u> from year 5 to year 10? Write the **rate of change** (five-year growth rate) as a ratio with units.

   c)   Compare the <u>ratio</u> you wrote in part (b) to the ratio you wrote in part (e) of the previous problem. What do you notice? What conjecture can you make?

   d)   If the bottom of the sign for the museum is 35 feet above the ground, how many years will it take for the trees to reach the sign?

   e)   If the sign is 12 feet tall, in how many years will the trees block it?

CB-15. One of the overflow parking lots at the old baseball stadium holds 280 cars. Corey is working as a parking lot attendant at the overflow lot. His shift will end when the lot is emptied. The baseball game is sold out, so the overflow lot is full.

a) Assuming that cars leave at the same rate, copy and complete the table below. Write the rule for the relationship.

Time in Minutes (x)	0	3	6	9	12	x
Number of Cars in Lot (y)	280	247	214			

b) What is the change in the x-values? What is the change in the y-values?

c) Use your answers in part (b) to write a ratio to express the rate that the number of cars in the lot changes. Is this a positive or negative rate? Be sure to include units and simplify your ratio.

d) Compare your ratio and your equation. Which part of the equation shows the rate of change?

e) Graph the information from the table. Label the line with its equation. Describe the direction of your graph.

f) Make a conjecture about the rate of change between any two points on your line.

g) If Corey's shift ends when there are no more cars on the lot, at what time will Corey's shift be over if the game ends at 3:30 p.m.?

CB-16. Antoinette had a carton with a dozen eggs in it. She weighed the carton with different numbers of eggs and got the weights shown in the table below.

Number of eggs	12	9	6	3
Weight (ounces)	43	34	25	16

a) Make a graph showing the weight of the eggs vs. the number in the carton.

b) Looking at your graph, find the rate at which the weight increases as the number of eggs increases.

c) Where does the line cross the y-axis?

d) What is the meaning of where the line crosses the y-axis?

CB-17.

RATE OF CHANGE

RATE OF CHANGE is a ratio that compares the amount one quantity changes as another quantity changes.

$$\text{Rate of Change} = \frac{\text{change in one quantity}}{\text{change in the other quantity}}$$

In your Tool Kit highlight the formula for rate of change.

CB-18. As you move from left to right along the hypotenuse of each triangle, which one is going up? Which one is going down?

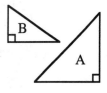

CB-19. Sherice can fill lemonade cups at a rate of four cups per minute.

a) How many cups can she fill in 6 minutes?

b) How many cups can she fill in 10 minutes?

c) If Sherice fills c cups in t minutes, write an equation which relates c and t.

d) Sketch a graph to show the relationship between time and the number of cups filled. Which value is on the horizontal axis? Which value is on the vertical axis? Label your graph.

CB-20. You are given two values in the following table. Assuming that the rate of change is constant, complete the table.

x	-6	-3	0	3	6	9	12	15	x
y			2	0					

a) How can you tell from the table if the graph is a line or a curve?

b) Graph the relationship in the table.

c) Describe the direction of the line.

d) Calculate the rate of change between $x = 0$ and $x = 3$. Remember the formula for rate of change: $\text{rate of change} = \frac{\text{change in y-values}}{\text{change in x-values}}$.

e) Calculate the rate of change between $x = -3$ and $x = 9$.

f) Identify the x- and y-intercepts.

CB-21. Use the symbol < or > to complete the following inequalities.

a) -16   -19   b) |-18| -11   c) -12   0

CB-22. Martin finds a sweater for $39.99 plus tax. The tax rate is 8.25%. If Martin has $42, does he have enough money to buy the sweater?

CB-23. Armand and Benito want to go to the camp store to buy snacks for their hike. They pull the change out of their pockets and find that they have a total of $2.50. Benito notices th they have twice as many dimes as they have nickels and two more quarters than nickels. Write an equation that represents the total amount of money they have in terms of nickel Find out how many nickels, dimes, and quarters they have to spend on their snacks. A Guess and Check table might help you get started.

CB-24. For the following problem, you will need your graph from problem CB-13. Follow the steps below and use the graph to find the rate of change between the age of a tree and its height.

a) Plot and label points A(2, 7) and B(5, 13).

b) Draw a right triangle that has segment AB as its hypotenuse. This right triangle that helps you determine the rate of change between any two points on the line is called a **slope triangle**.

c) Find the number of feet the trees have grown between points A and B.

d) Find the number of years that have elapsed between points A and B.

e) Find the rate of change between the points A and B on the graph.

CB-25. Repeat the process in the previous problem for the points C(1, 5) and D(7, 17) to find th slope of the line through the points C and D.

CB-26. Imagine any two points on the line passing through the points A, B, C, and D in the previous problems. What would be the slope of the line (rate of change) between any two points on the line? Give a reason for your answer.

CB-27.   Read the following information and use it to answer the questions that follow.

CALCULATING THE SLOPE OF A LINE

You can calculate the slope of a line using the same methods you used to find the rate of change.

1.   Pick any two points on the line.

2.   Draw a slope triangle.

3.   Use the slope triangle to find the <u>vertical</u> change between the first and second points along the y-axis.

4.   Use the slope triangle to find the <u>horizontal</u> change between the first and second points along the x-axis

5.   Use the equation $slope = \dfrac{change\ in\ y\text{-}values}{change\ in\ x\text{-}values}$. Substitute the values from steps 3 and 4.

6.   If the graph goes up from left to right, the slope ratio is positive. If the line goes down from left to right, the slope ratio is negative.

Use the method above to help you find the slopes of the following lines. Identify the x- and y-intercepts for each line.

a)   b)

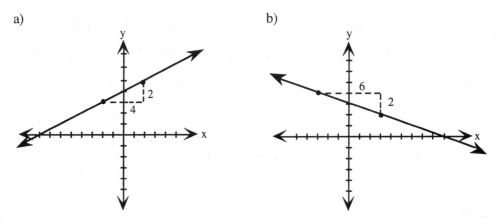

>>**Problem continues on the next page.>>**

c)

d)

e)

f)

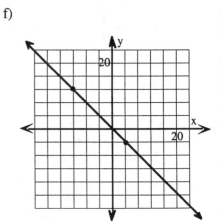

CB-28. Several lines are graphed on the set of axes below right. For each line locate one point where the line crosses exactly through the corner of a graph paper square as it does at the origin. Use this point to find the rate of change (slope) and complete the table on the resource page provided by your teacher. Compare the results of the two columns for each equation.

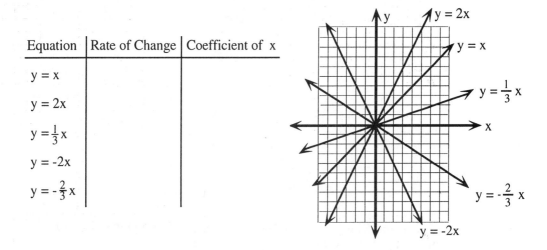

Equation	Rate of Change	Coefficient of x
$y = x$		
$y = 2x$		
$y = \frac{1}{3}x$		
$y = -2x$		
$y = -\frac{2}{3}x$		

CB-29. Find the slope of each line segment below.

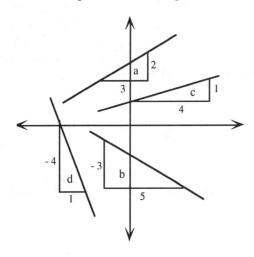

CB-30. Evaluate.

a) $-44 - 55$

b) $100 + (-60)$

c) $83 - (-15)$

d) $34 - 42$

e) $-11(-10)$

f) $285 + (-642)$

CB-31.   Find the perimeter and area of each figure.

a)   b)   c)

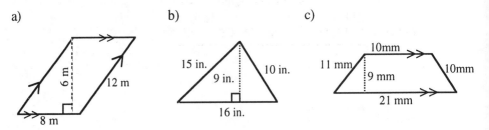

CB-32.   Solve for x.

a) $\frac{2}{3}x + \frac{2}{3} = \frac{2}{3}$ b) $x + \frac{3}{4} = 3\frac{2}{3}$

CB-33.   A toy car cost $1.89 before a television special. After the television special, the price jumped to $2.50. By what percent did the price increase?

CB-34.   Determine the compound interest earned on $220.00 invested at 3.25% compounded annually for 6 years.

CB-35.   A number pattern begins -5, -3, etc. with the numbers increasing by 2 each time. The sum of the reciprocals of the terms is $\frac{16}{63}$. How many terms are in the pattern?

CB-36.   Use what you have learned in the past few problems to figure out the slope of the line for each of the following linear equations. Also decide whether the graph of each line is increasing or decreasing.

a) $y = \frac{1}{2}x + 2$ b) $y = 2x - 4$ c) $y = -\frac{1}{3}x + 4$

d)   Which graph goes up most steeply? Which goes down most steeply?

CB-37.   Below right are the graphs of five equations. Use the graphs and the equations to
          complete the table. The "constant" is the term in the equation without the variable.

Equation	Constant	Coordinate of y-intercept
$y = x$		
$y = x + 2$		
$y = x + 5$		
$y = x - 2$		
$y = x - 6$		

CB-38.   Use the table in the previous problem and compare the y-intercept of each line to the constant
          number in each equation. What is the relationship between the y-intercept of
          the line and the equation?

SLOPE OF A LINE AND LINEAR EQUATIONS

The **SLOPE** of a line is the rate of change between any two points on that line. It represents both steepness and direction. The slope ratio states the rate at which the relation between the two quantities is changing. The sign of the ratio indicates whether the rate of change is increasing (+) or decreasing (–).

$$\textbf{slope} = \frac{\text{vertical change}}{\text{horizontal change}} = \frac{\text{change in y-values}}{\text{change in x-values}}$$

Some textbooks write the ratio $\frac{\text{vertical change}}{\text{horizontal change}}$ as $\frac{\text{rise}}{\text{run}}$.

All equations of straight lines can be put in the form

$$y = (\textbf{coefficient})x + (\textbf{constant number})$$

where the **coefficient of x** is the rate of change (or **slope**), and the **constant number** is the **y-intercept**.

This form of a linear equation is called the **SLOPE-INTERCEPT FORM** and is written $y = mx + b$, where m is the slope and b is the y-coordinate of the y-intercept $(0, b)$.

Example:

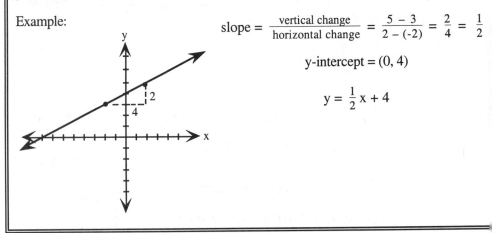

$$\text{slope} = \frac{\text{vertical change}}{\text{horizontal change}} = \frac{5-3}{2-(-2)} = \frac{2}{4} = \frac{1}{2}$$

$$\text{y-intercept} = (0, 4)$$

$$y = \frac{1}{2}x + 4$$

In your Tool Kit, highlight:

a)   the words in the ratio that tell you how to find slope.

b)   the slope and y-intercept (found in the example).

CB-40. Use what you have learned in the past few problems to find the y-intercept of each of the following equations.

a) $y = 2x - 4$ b) $y = \frac{1}{2}x + 2$ c) $y = -\frac{1}{3}x + 4$

d) $y = 3x + 1$ e) $y = -\frac{3}{2}x + 5$ f) $y = \frac{3}{4}x - 3$

g) Which graph goes up most steeply? Which goes down most steeply?

CB-41. Use the scale graph at right with the three points A(0, 250), B(150, 600), and C(150, 250) to answer the following questions.

a) What kind of triangle is ΔABC?

b) What is the distance from A to C? C to B?

c) What is the slope of line AB?

d) Write the equation of the line.

e) What is the distance from A to B?

f) What is the area of ΔABC?

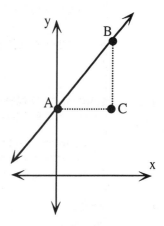

CB-42. The groundskeeper of the arena kept track of the temperature from 6 a.m. to 6 p.m. during a day with a short heavy rain. He recorded the temperature every hour. Study his graph and use it to answer the questions below.

a) When did the temperature increase?

b) When did the temperature increase most quickly? Explain how you know.

c) When did the temperature decrease? Explain how you know.

d) What was the rate of change of the temperature from 4 p.m. to 6 p.m.? Show your work.

Temperature for March 15

CB-43.   The local donut shop has an automatic donut machine that makes dozens of donuts per hour. The table below shows the number of donuts made throughout the day up to different times.

Time	7:00	7:30	8:00	8:30	9:00
Number of Donuts	1280	1520	1760	2000	2240

a)   Draw a graph showing the number of donuts made in relation to the time. Scale the y-axis using an interval size of 200. Let 0 time on the x-axis represent 6:00 a.m.

b)   At what rate does the machine produce donuts?

c)   Where does the line cross the y-axis?

d)   What is the meaning of where the line crosses the y-axis?

CB-44.   What time does the donut shop in the previous problem start making donuts?

CB-45.   Al bought a computer for $2200 in July. Now the same model sells for $1650. By what percent did the price decrease?

CB-46.   Use proportions to solve the problem below. Show all steps.

Ray bought 36 feet of wire for $24. How much will he have to pay for 90 feet of wire? How many feet of wire can he buy for $150?

CB-47.   Determine the simple interest earned on $118.00 invested at 5.25% for 8 years.

CB-48.   Solve the following equations.

a) $4x + (-3) = -27$ b) $3(2x - 3) = -15$

c) $21 = 2(x + 4)$ d) $2(2x - 15) = -20$

e) $4(x + 2) = 2x - 9$ f) $x + (-7) = 3(x + (-2))$

CB-49.   Use the equation $y = \frac{3}{2}x + 1$ to complete parts (a) through (d) below.

   a)   Make a table and complete it. Use integer values for x from -3 to 3.

   b)   Graph the equation using the values from your table.

   c)   What is the rate of change as determined by the table?

   d)   What is the slope of the line?

   e)   What is the y-intercept of the line?

CB-50.   For each of the following equations, identify the slope and y-intercept. Then tell whether the line will have a positive or negative slope and what this says about the line.

   a) $y = 3x + 6$ b) $y = -\frac{4}{5}x + 2$ c) $y = 0.75x - 4$ d) $y = -\frac{1}{3}x$

CB-51.   Ping and Xiu were graphing some lines for homework when Ping noticed that Xiu was working much more quickly than he was. Ping asked Xiu to show him her shortcut.

   Xiu explained, "If you want to graph $y = \frac{1}{2}x + 2$, just start by putting a point at 2 on the y-axis for the y-intercept, and then counting up one and over two to the right. The 'up one and over two' comes from the rate of change $\frac{1}{2}$ in the equation."

   Use Xiu's shortcut to graph the equations below on the same set of axes.

   a) $y = -\frac{1}{3}x + 4$ b) $y = \frac{5}{3}x - 2$ c) $y = \frac{3}{4}x + 1$

CB-52.   Use Xiu's shortcut to graph the equation $y = -\frac{2}{3}x + 2$. Label the line with its equation.

CB-53.   Points A, B, and C lie on the same line.

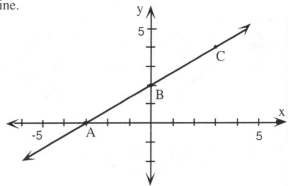

a)   Using points A and B, draw the slope triangle to find the slope of the line.

b)   Using points B and C, draw the slope triangle to find the slope of the line.

c)   Using points A and C, draw the slope triangle to find the slope of the line.

d)   Which of the points on a line should you use to find its slope? Explain your answer

e)   Identify the x- and y-intercepts.

f)   Write an equation for this line. What part of the equation shows the slope of the line? How does the other part of the equation relate to the graph?

CB-54.   The last soccer game of the season has been scheduled to start at 1:00 p.m. at the arena. A special celebration will follow the game. Gary and his two friends have tickets to the game and have agreed to meet at the stadium. They all decided to leave their houses at noon and meet in the parking lot.

Gary lives 20 miles from the arena. Due to traffic, he can only average about 40 miles per hour.

Luis lives only 5 miles from the arena. He decides to ride his bicycle to avoid the traffic. He averages about 6 miles per hour on his bike.

Leonard lives 15 miles from the arena. He manages to avoid all traffic, averaging 45 miles per hour for the trip.

a)   Make a table for each person above, showing the distance they have traveled at each time. Let x represent time (in minutes) and y represent the distance from the arena.

	Minutes	0	10	20	30	40	50
Distance from Arena	Gary	20					
	Luis	5					
	Leonard	15					

b)   Construct a single graph. Let the x-axis represent time (in minutes) and the y-axis distance (in miles) from the arena. Let 1 grid mark equal 2 units (either miles or minutes). Graph all three trips on the same graph in different colors.

c)   What is the slope of the line for each person (rate of change)?

d)   Will they all arrive in time for the 1 p.m. celebration? Explain.

CB-55.   Complete the following Diamond Problems.

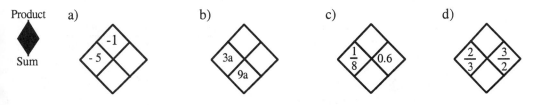

Product   a)

Sum

b)

c)

d)

CB-56.   Identify the slope and y-intercept of these linear equations. Use them to graph lines
without making a table.

a) $y = \frac{1}{2}x - 5$

b) $y = -\frac{5}{3}x + 4$

c) $y = 3x - 4$

CB-57.   Solve for x.

a) $\frac{2}{3}x = 45$

b) $\frac{3}{5}x = 60$

c) $2x + 3 = -x + 8$

d) $8 = -4 + 3(3x + 5)$

CB-58.   Ms. Beade had each team in her class measure the length of a team member's pencil.
The class was divided into seven teams, so there were seven measurements (in
centimeters): 7.5, 13.2, 17.0, 6.5, 9.8, 8.7, and 9.3. Use the data to:

a)   prepare a stem-and-leaf plot.

b)   prepare a box-and-whisker plot.

CB-59. Several lines are graphed on the axes below. Using your previous observations about rates of change, match each line to an equation in the table on the resource page.

Equation	Line
$y = 2x - 5$	____
$y = 4x + 2$	____
$y = -2x + 5$	____
$y = -3x - 2$	____
$y = -x + 8$	____

CB-60. Hank's great-great-grandfather buried a gold piece that was worth $2 in 1890. Suppose it doubled in value every 10 years that it was buried.

a) How much would it be worth in 2000?

Date (year)	1890	1900	1910									2000
Value ($)	2											

b) Add another row to your table and write your answers in exponential notation.

Exponent Form	2^1			2^4								

c) Graph the data. Put the date on the horizontal (x) axis and the value on the vertical (y) axis. Scale your axes appropriately.

d) Does it make sense to connect the points here?

CB-61. A survey was conducted before the last student council election, and 350 out of 900 students said they would vote for Jamie. One out of how many students said they wou[ ] vote for Jamie?

CHAPTER

B-62. Victor took his skateboard to the repair shop last week to get it fixed. The woman from the repair shop called at 5:00 p.m. to tell Victor that his skateboard was fixed and ready to be picked up. Victor wants to pick up his skateboard today before the repair shop closes at 5:30 p.m. It is now 5:10 p.m. and the repair shop is across town, $4\frac{1}{2}$ miles from Victor's house. Victor can ride his bicycle to the shop at an average speed of 15 miles per hour. Will Victor be able to pick up his skateboard today? Show how you get your answer.

B-63. George and Ben are two friends who make extra money parking cars at concerts and sporting events at the big arena near their homes in Indianapolis. They both want to go to college to become architects. Ben wants to go to Indiana-Purdue University at Fort Wayne, but George wants to start at the local community college and transfer in two years. Both are worried about the expense of college since neither of their families can afford to help.

Ben's older sister, Marie, says that in her job they use graphs to estimate. She will show George how to use these ideas to decide if he will have enough money to attend college. She uses Ben's savings book to show George how to do it. Here is how to use Marie's idea.

Month	Feb.	Mar.	April	May	June	July	Aug.	Sept.	Oct.	Nov.
Balance	$61	$179	$285	$401	$524	$627	$748	$857	$971	$1085

a) Make a scatter plot showing the balance in Ben's savings account on the first of each month. Let February be Month 0 on your graph.

b) Use a ruler to draw a line of best fit (a straight line that goes through the "middle" of the pattern of the points) for the months from February through November. What is the slope of the line of best fit? What does this slope represent?

c) About how much can Ben be expected to save if he works through August 1 of next year?

B-64. George did not start parking cars until July 1, when he had $209 in his savings account. Here is a list of his monthly savings balances.

Month	July	Aug.	Sept.	Oct.	Nov.
Balance	$209	$334	$451	$581	$706

a) Make a scatter plot showing the balance in George's savings account on the first of each month. Let July be Month 0 on the graph.

b) Draw a line of best fit for the months from July through November. What is the slope of your line? What does this slope represent?

c) George is going to keep working at the arena until college starts in August. If George saves about the same amount each month, how much will he save by August 1 of next year?

CB-65. George's school counselor gave him a sheet with information about expenses at Indianapolis Community College. George has qualified for a Pell Grant. In the last problem, he got a reasonable estimate of how much he will save during the year parking cars. Use that information and the information at right to determine if he has enough money yet to afford to attend the community college.

Community College	
Costs	
Tuition (1 year)	$1986
Books	600
Gas for car + parking	800
Clothes, personal, etc.	900
Total Cost	$4286
Sources of Income	
Pell Grant	$2100
Savings(from arena job)	
Total Income	

CB-66. Ben's school counselor calculated the expenses at Indiana-Purdue University at Fort Wayne (IPFW) including tuition, books, housing, and some personal spending money. You estimated how much money he will save parking cars through the year. He has received a Pell Grant and has qualified for a $3025 loan. How much more will he need to save?

IPFW	
Total Cost	$8818
Sources of Income	
Pell Grant	$2400
Loan	$3025
Savings (from arena job)	
Total Income	

CB-67. George has been offered a second job for next summer that will not interfere with his arena job. He will net $6 per hour helping a friend sweep out stores. Calculate how many hours George will need to work at this rate to have enough money for college.

CB-68. If Ben needs to earn about $1300, how many hours will he need to work at $6 per hour?

CB-69. What is the slope of the equation $y = \frac{3}{5}x + 2$? Where would this graph cross the y-axis? Explain.

CB-70. Calculate the following sums and differences.

a) $3\frac{1}{2} + 2\frac{5}{8}$

b) $\frac{26}{11} + 7$

c) $5 - 1\frac{10}{13}$

CHAPTER

CB-71.   Use the graph at right to describe the
savings habits of each student. For
example, from the graph you know that
Rhonda starts with $4 and Lauren saves
$3 every two weeks.

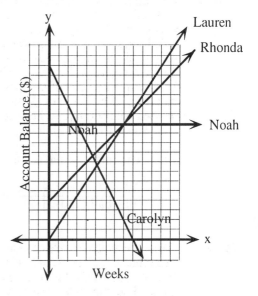

CB-72.   Ray Sheo keeps track of the height of his fast-growing corn. His records are shown in
the table below.

Day	0	2	4	6	8	x
Height (cm)	2	7.5	13	18.5	24	

a)   What is the growth rate of Ray's corn? Is this number always the same?

b)   If you graph the points in this table, will it make a line or a curve? Explain how
you know.

c)   In how many days will the corn be 47 centimeters tall?

d)   If Ray harvests the corn when it reaches 3 meters, when will he harvest it?

CB-73.   The simplified form of $\left(\frac{8+6}{7}\right) - 7$ is:

(A) 5   (B) 1   (C) -5   (D) 2

CB-74.   Solve for x.

a) $3x + 2(x - 6) = 3x + 8$ b) $3 - 4(x + 1) = 12x + 3$ c) $0.8x = 68$

CB-75.   Lucian is driving to Fort Lauderdale. Assuming he averages 52 mph, determine how f
         he has gone after the following amounts of time.

    a)   3 hours   b)   6 hours   c) $\frac{1}{2}$ hour   d) $4\frac{1}{2}$ hours

CB-76.   Joshua wants to have a huge collection of baseball cards. Currently he has 175 cards.
         His plan is to use his allowance to buy a pack of 12 cards each week.

    a)   The current week is 0 in the table below. Complete the table.

Week	0	1	2	3	4	5
Baseball Cards	175					

    b)   Calculate the rate of change. Is the graph a
          line?

    c)   From the table, can you determine the
          y-intercept? How do you know?

    d)   Write an equation to represent the total number
          of cards (y) in terms of weeks (x).

CB-77.   Follow your teacher's directions for practicing mental math.

CB-78.   Use the inequality signs to answer the following problems.

    a)   -3 ___ 2   b)   -3 ___ -6

    c)   0 ___ -7   d)   -2 ___ 0 ___ 7

CB-79.   You have been working with the < and > signs. We can modify the signs to include
         the possibility that the two values are equal: ≤ and ≥. The ≤ sign means less than or
         equal to. The ≥ sign means greater than or equal to.

         For example, $x \geq 6$ means x is greater than 6 or equal to 6. This is how it is graphed
         on a number line:

         Graph each inequality:

    a) $x \geq 5$ b) $x \leq 5$

CB-80.   Ben told Marie that he had an amount of money in his wallet that was less than $20. He asked her how to write this as an inequality. Marie said, "The amount of money you have is unknown to me, so let's call it x. The symbol for 'less than' looks like this: <, so write x < 20." On a number line, x < 20 looks like this:

$$-20 \quad 0 \quad 20$$

a)   Graph the following problems using Marie's method.

i)   x = 5   ii)   x > 5

iii)   x < 5   iv)   x ≥ 5

b)   How are graphs (ii) and (iv) different?

c)   What does the filled-in circle mean?

d)   What does the open circle mean?

CB-81.   Ben asked Marie how to decide which way to draw the arrows for the inequality x ≥ 6. She told him that to decide which direction the arrow goes, first locate the point, 6, on the number line. Next check to see whether 5 or 7 makes the inequality true, since each of these numbers is located on a different side of 6.

a)   Is 5 ≥ 6?   b)   Is 7 ≥ 6?

The arrow goes toward 7, since 7 made the inequality true.

CB-82.   The temperature for the day is predicted to be no higher than 75° F and no lower than 50° F. This graph represents the inequality 50° ≤ x ≤ 75°.

$$25 \quad 30 \quad 35 \quad 40 \quad 45 \quad 50 \quad 55 \quad 60 \quad 65 \quad 70 \quad 75 \quad 80$$

a)   What do you think this graph means?

b)   What would the graph for the inequality 45° < x ≤ 70° look like?

CB-83.   Corey's car needs 12 gallons of gas to go 220 miles.

a)   How much gas is needed to go 0 miles?

b)   Construct a graph that shows g, the number of gallons of gas used (y-axis), compared to m, the number of miles driven (x-axis).

c)   Using your graph, estimate how much gas will be needed to go 70 miles.

d)   Estimate how many miles can be driven with 10 gallons of gas.

e)   Use proportions to find exact answers to parts (c) and (d).

f)   How many miles per gallon does Corey's car get? Show your work.

CB-84.   Corey wanted to be able to figure out how much gas it would take him to go a certain number of miles. He decided he would rather write and solve the linear equation than solve a proportion.

a)   Knowing that he could go 220 miles on 12 gallons of gas, use your knowledge of proportions and slope to write the equation that represents this. Use x for miles and y for gallons.

b)   What is the slope of the equation? Compare the slope with the proportions in part (e) of problem CB-83. What do you notice?

CB-85.   George had to buy a book for a class he needed to take to study for college entrance exams. Marie told him that the cost of the book was at least $10 but no more than $20. Write the possible cost of the book as an inequality.

CB-86.   Ben's school needed vans for a field trip. Each van can hold no more than 9 students. Make a number line graph to show the number of students that can travel in a van. Remember that $x \le 9$ and that no van can have part of a student.

a)   Discuss with your partner whether your graph should have a line with an arrow or something different.

b)   Describe what your graph looks like.

CB-87. Graph the following inequalities.

a) $x \geq 6$

b) $x < -7$

c) $0 \leq x \leq 8$ for all whole numbers

d) $-7 < x \leq 10$

CB-88. The answers in this problem are not numerical. Use the variables a, b, c, and/or d to answer each question.

a)   What are the coordinates of F?

b)   What are the coordinates of G?

c)   What is the area of ΔAHG?

d)   What is the slope of segment AG?

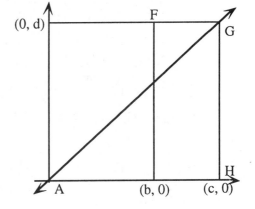

CB-89. On a piece of graph paper, plot the following points and connect them: A(-3, -4), B(2, 4), and C(5, -4).

a)   What is the area of ΔABC?

b)   What is the perimeter of ΔABC?

c)   Calculate the slope of each side of the triangle.

CB-90. Evaluate.

a) $18 \cdot 2 + 3 \cdot 2 \div 6 + |-6|$ b) $27 - |-3 \cdot 7|$ c) $3 + 6 \cdot 9 - 3 \cdot 5$

d) $-11 + 4 \cdot 7 - |11|$ e) $13 - 2 \cdot 6 + 3^2 \cdot 4$ f) $3 \cdot 7 - (4 \cdot 2)^2 + 6^2 \cdot 2$

CB-91. Solve these problems. Show your steps.

a) $2x - 8 = |26|$

b) $3x + 5 = |-20|$

c) $4x + 12 = 32$

d) $8x - 16 = -32$

CB-92. Ben's little sister, Clarisse, came home with a math problem she could not do. She asked Ben to help her.

The problem was $x + 4 \geq 10$. She told Ben that she could solve equations but not inequalities. Ben told her that solving inequalities is a lot like solving equations. Here is Ben's method.

- Write the inequality as an equation and solve in the usual way:
  $x + 4 = 10$, so $x = 6$.

- Put a solid dot at $x = 6$
  on a number line.

- Test (substitute) a point in the <u>original</u> inequality to see if it makes the inequality true. Zero is one of the easiest numbers to test: $0 + 4 \geq 10 \Rightarrow 4 \geq 10$, which is false.

- Since 0 made the inequality false and 0 is to the left of 6, all points to the right of 6 must be true for $x + 4 \geq 10$, so draw a line with an arrow to the right of 6.

The graph shows the solution, $x \geq 6$.

CB-93. Solve and graph these problems.

a) $x + 5 > 7$ b) $7 > x + 5$

c) $x - 6 \geq -12$ d) $2x - 8 \leq 26$

e) $8 - 2x \leq -26$ f) $3x + 5 \leq |-20|$

g) $4x + 12 < 32$ h) $16 - 8x < -32$

CB-94. Kindra would like to have more than $1500 in her savings account.

a) If she starts with $61 in her savings account, write an inequality to show how much she wants to have.

b) Solve the inequality in part (a).

c) How much does Kindra need to save?

CB-95. The new Olympic-sized pool is closed for its annual cleaning and only about 10,000 gallons of water are left in the bottom. It is time to refill it. The pool holds 640,000 gallons and can be filled by the usual pipes at 2000 gallons per minute. A fire hose can also be used to pump up to another 1000 gallons per minute if desired.

   a)   What are the minimum and maximum rates of filling the pool?

   b)   Find the shortest and longest times it can take to fill the pool.

   c)   On the same set of axes, draw two lines that show the possible amounts of water in the pool after x minutes. Be sure to show where the pool is full.

   d)   Write the equations of the lines you drew in part (c).

CB-96. Solve and graph the following inequalities.

   a) $2x + 5 \geq 10$ b) $4 \leq x - 2$

   c) $3x - 9 < -12$ d) $-12 < x - 9$

CB-97. Graph these lines on the same set of axes.

   a) $y = \frac{3}{5}x - 4$ b) $y = -\frac{1}{2}x + 1$

CB-98. Gail bought her cap for $7.50, which was $\frac{1}{3}$ off the original price. What was the original price? (Hint: What part of the original price is $7.50?)

CB-99. Solve the following equations.

   a) $5x + 4 = 3x + 2.5$ b) $\frac{3}{4}x - 3 = -5$ c) $-\frac{2}{5}x - 1 = 9$

CB-100. A prism is 23.5 inches tall. The base of the prism is a right triangle with legs that are 5 inches and 3.75 inches long. Draw and label a diagram. What is the volume and surface area of the prism? Show your subproblems.

CB-101.   Use the graph below to answer the following questions.

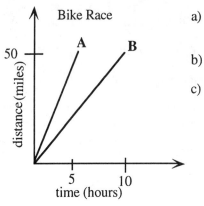

a)   Which bicyclist, the one at point A or the one at point B, is traveling at the greater rate?

b)   Find the coordinates of point A and point B.

c)   What is the average rate in miles per hour for the bicyclist at point A? What is the average rate for the bicyclist at point B?

CB-102.   In 45 minutes, Ishmael can ride his bicycle 12 miles. Assume he rides at a steady rate.

a)   How long does it take him to ride 4 miles?

b)   How far will he ride in 60 minutes if he continues at the same rate of speed?

c)   What is Ishmael's average speed in miles per hour?

CB-103. **Chapter Summary**

It is time to summarize and review what you have learned in this chapter. In teams or with a partner, you will be making a mobile. Choose examples from the chapter for the following topics: slope, rate of change, y-intercept, and inequalities.

Your team should divide the work in order to complete the mobile in one class period. For each topic, the mobile must have a concept label and a sample problem. See the example at right. You may put the four topics back to back to get all of them on one mobile.

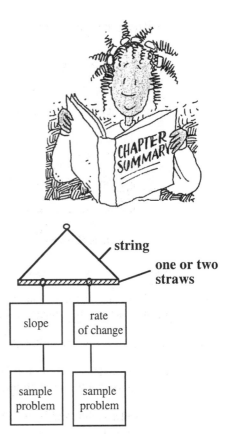

CB-104. Mai has a small bottle with 2 cups of orange juice. While waiting for chemistry lab to start, she pours out different amounts and then weighs the bottle and the juice left in it. Here are the weights she recorded.

Number of Cups Left in Bottle	2	$1\frac{3}{4}$	1	$\frac{1}{2}$
Weight (in ounces)	21	$16\frac{3}{2}$	12	$7\frac{1}{2}$

a)   Draw a graph showing the weight vs. the number of cups left in the bottle.

b)   Find the slope of the line you drew in part (a). Is the slope positive or negative?

c)   What does the slope represent?

d)   Where is the y-intercept?

e)   What is the meaning of the y-intercept?

CB-105. Complete the table below for the equation $y = -|x + 4| - 3$.

x	-6	-4	-1	0	2	3	5
y							

a) Predict the shape and orientation of the graph.

b) Graph the equation.

c) Was your prediction in part (a) correct? What part of the equation determined the orientation of the graph?

CB-106. Brian's Sports Memorabilia Company puts together specialized packages with clothing and equipment from the customer's favorite sports team. The company can put together packages at a constant rate. An order has been placed for 100 packages. Each package costs $750. The company inventory for April is listed below.

Day	3	6	9		
Completed Packages	42	44	46		

a) Fill in the next two sets of data.

b) What is the rate of change (packages/day)?

c) What is the shape of the graph?

d) What is the slope of the line?

e) What is the y-intercept of the line?

f) What does the y-intercept represent in this problem?

g) What is the equation of the line?

h) How many days will it take to have 100 packages completed?

CB-107. A line is determined by the points (1, 2) and (2, -1).

a) Draw a slope triangle and determine the slope.

b) Use the slope pattern to find another point on the line with integer coordinates.

c) Find the distance between the first two points.

CB-108.   For each line find the slope, the y-intercept, and give the equation.

a)   b)

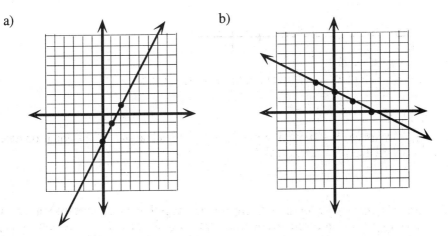

CB-109.   Use the slope and y-intercept to graph each line.

   a) $y = -\frac{2}{3}x - 1$ b) $y = \frac{1}{2}x + 2$ c) $y = 3x$

CB-110.   Why can't you use slope-intercept form to graph $y = x^2 - 2$?

CB-111.   Graph each inequality.

   a) $x \geq 3$ b) $x < -2$ c) $-2 \leq x < 3$

CB-112.   Solve and graph each inequality.

   a) $2x + 1 \leq 5$ b) $7 > 3 - x$ c) $3x + 7 > x - 1$

CB-113.   On a set of axes scaled by tens,

   a)   Plot the points (-24, 40) and (36, 60). Use a ruler to draw the line between them.

   b)   Estimate the y-intercept.

   c)   Draw a slope triangle to find the slope of the line.

   d)   What is the equation of the line?

CB-114. **What We Have Done in This Chapter**

Below is a list of the Tool Kit entries from this chapter.

- CB-17   Rate of Change

- CB-39   Slope of a Line and Linear Equations

Review all the entries and read the notes you made in your Tool Kit. Make a list of any questions, terms, or notes you do not understand. Ask your partner or study team members for help. If anything is still unclear, ask your teacher.

Modeling Growth

Chapter 10

Chapter 10
Modeling Growth: EXPONENTS, SCIENTIFIC NOTATION, AND VOLUME

This chapter brings the course to a close by using several ideas with three-dimensional figures. You will have the opportunity to apply scale factors to create enlargements and reductions of items you select. This project will reinforce previous work with surface area and volume. Your teacher will give you detailed directions about this project; for now, begin to look for an everyday item like a cereal box, bar of soap, canister of snack foods, or similar items that you would like to use for the enlargement and reduction project in this chapter. You will need to have your selection approved by your teacher.

You will also continue to use subproblems to practice various topics in multi-step problems. Finally, you will tie together the notion of exponents and apply them to large and small numbers.

In this chapter you will have the opportunity to:

- work with very large and very small numbers.

- simplify exponential expressions.

- investigate the change in volume of three-dimensional figures when the dimensions are enlarged or reduced.

- investigate growth patterns of surface area and volume in relation to increases and decreases in dimensions.

- study the graphs of equations containing squared and cubed numbers.

Read the problem below, but **do not try to solve it now**. What you learn over the next few days will enable you to solve it.

MG-0.   **Cracker Snacks**

The Clifford Snack Company produces cracker canisters. Their snack-size canisters are similar to full-size canisters but have been reduced by a scale factor of $\frac{2}{5}$. Use the dimensions of the full-size canisters to calculate the surface area and volume of both the full-size and the snack-size canisters.

Chapter 10

Modeling Growth: EXPONENTS, SCIENTIFIC NOTATION, AND VOLUME

MG-1.   Use the set of cube template resource pages your teacher gives your team to make six cubes of different sizes. Do not seal the lids shut, because the cubes need to be nested for storage. When you finish, write in your notebook, "Cubes built."

MG-2.   Get the Cube Growth resource page from your teacher. Record the scale factors and edge lengths for Cubes A through F. For this problem we will agree that Cube C (the colored one) has an edge length of one unit. Thinking about how many edge lengths of Cube C fit along the side of Cube D will help you fill in the table. Then complete parts (a) and (b) below.

Name of Cube	Scale Factor	Length of One Edge	Surface Area of One Face	Volume of Cube
A				
B				
C (Unit Cube)	$\frac{1}{1}$	1 unit	1 unit ^{2}	1 unit ^{3}
D				
E				
F				
Rule				
Extensions				

a)   Complete the remaining columns for cubes A through F. You will find it easier to begin with cubes D through F and leave cubes A and B for last.

b)   Using the patterns developed in the Cube Growth resource page, write a rule for each column in terms of x. Then use those rules to complete the remaining rows in the table.

MG-3.   Use the rectangular prism shown below right to complete parts (a) through (d) below.

a)   Calculate the surface area of the prism. Show all your subproblems.

b)   Explain why the exponent for area is 2 (that is, cm^2).

c)   Calculate the volume of the prism.

d)   Explain why the exponent for volume is a 3 (that is, cm^3).

MG-4.   Copy and complete the chart of these cubed numbers.

Exponent Form	Factored Form	Standard Form
2^3	$2 \cdot 2 \cdot 2$	8
3^3		
	$4 \cdot 4 \cdot 4$	
		125
6^3		
7^3		
	$8 \cdot 8 \cdot 8$	
9^3		

MG-5.   Copy and complete the table below.

Original Form	Factored Form	Simplified Form
$5^2 \cdot 5^5$	$(5 \cdot 5)(5 \cdot 5 \cdot 5 \cdot 5 \cdot 5)$	5^7
$2^2 \cdot 2^4$		
$3^7 \cdot 3^2$		
$x^3 \cdot x^5$		
$x^3y^2 \cdot xy^2$		

a)   For each example, compare the bases of the original expression to the base(s) of th simplified expression. What do you notice?

b)   For each example, compare the exponents of the original form to the exponent(s) o the simplified form. What do you notice?

c)   Simplify $20^{12} \cdot 20^{51}$ without writing the factored form. Describe your process.

MG-6.   State the slope and y-intercept for the equation of each line below.

a) $y = -\frac{5}{3}x - 2$ b) $y = 4x - \frac{5}{12}$

MG-7.   Solve each inequality and sketch the graph of the solution on a number line.

a) $4x - 10 < 6$ b) $3x - 4 \leq 5x - 8$

MG-8.   Is 3^5 the same as $3 \cdot 5$? Explain.

MG-9.   Now that we have started a new chapter, it is time for you to organize your binder.

a)   Put the work from the last chapter in order and keep it in a separate folder.

b)   When this is completed, write, "I have organized my binder."

MG-10.   Use the data in problem MG-2 to make three graphs on the large axes on the resource
page your teacher gives you. For this problem we will let each x-value represent a scale
factor and examine how it changes for length, area, and volume. Draw one graph
comparing scale factor to edge length, $y = x$ for $0 \le x \le 11$; one comparing scale factor
to area, $y = x^2$ for $0 \le x \le 11$; and one comparing scale factor to volume, $y = x^3$ for
$0 \le x \le 5$. You will need to calculate additional values for $x = 10$ and $x = 11$. Write
the rule by each graph, then complete parts (a) through (c) below.

a)   Which graph is the flattest when the scale factor is 5?

b)   Which graph is the steepest when the scale factor is 5?

c)   Explain why the curve for the volume data becomes so much steeper than the curve
for the surface area data.

MG-11.   Graph the three equations in the previous problem on the small axes on the resource page for
$0 \le x \le \frac{3}{2}$ for intervals of $\frac{1}{4}$. A data table is included for $x = \frac{3}{4}$, $x = \frac{5}{4}$, and $x = \frac{3}{2}$.

a)   What point(s) is (are) common to all three graphs?

b)   Why are the curves below the straight line $(y = x)$ for the scale factors $0 < x < 1$?

MG-12.   Label the dimensions of the prism at right where it appears on the resource page your teacher gives you.

Original
Prism

a)   Find the surface area and volume of the original prism. Record the results on your resource page.

b)   Label the dimensions of each of the enlargements. Use the scale factors $\frac{2}{1}$ and $\frac{3}{1}$.

c)   Calculate the surface area and volume for <u>each</u> of the two enlargements. Record your answers on the resource page.

d)   Write and simplify a ratio comparing the surface area of each enlargement to the surface area of the original.

e)   Write and simplify a ratio comparing the volume of each enlargement to the volume of the original.

f)   Continue sketching, labeling, and calculating the surface area and volume for prisms enlarged by the scale factors on the resource page.

MG-13.   Refer to your table in problem MG-2 to help you answer the questions below.

a)   How do the surface area ratios compare to the enlargement ratios?

b)   How do the volume ratios compare to the enlargement ratios?

c)   Compare your results in parts (a) and (b) to your graphs in problem MG-10.

RATIOS OF DIMENSIONAL CHANGE

For any pair of similar figures or solids with a scale factor $\frac{a}{b}$, the enlargement and reduction relationships are:

Length (one dimension)	Area (two dimensions)	Volume (three dimensions)
$\frac{a}{b}$	$\frac{a^2}{b^2}$	$\frac{a^3}{b^3}$

Example 1:   Example 2:

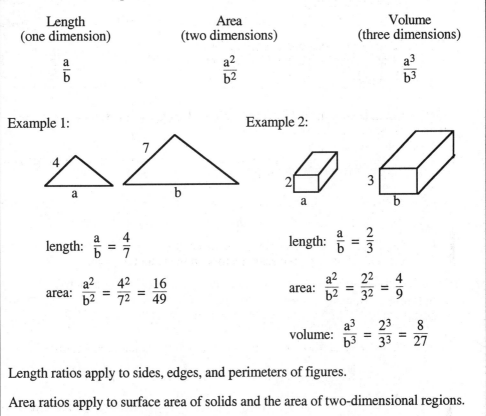

length: $\frac{a}{b} = \frac{4}{7}$

area: $\frac{a^2}{b^2} = \frac{4^2}{7^2} = \frac{16}{49}$

length: $\frac{a}{b} = \frac{2}{3}$

area: $\frac{a^2}{b^2} = \frac{2^2}{3^2} = \frac{4}{9}$

volume: $\frac{a^3}{b^3} = \frac{2^3}{3^3} = \frac{8}{27}$

Length ratios apply to sides, edges, and perimeters of figures.

Area ratios apply to surface area of solids and the area of two-dimensional regions.

Highlight the three basic ratios and their headings (length, area, and volume) in your Tool Kit.

MG-15.   Copy and complete the table. Use the Giant **1** to simplify the factored form.

Original Form	Factored Form	Simplified Form
$\dfrac{5^5}{5^2}$	$\dfrac{5 \cdot 5 \cdot 5 \cdot 5 \cdot 5}{5 \cdot 5}$	5^3
$\dfrac{2^4}{2^2}$		
$\dfrac{3^7}{3^4}$		
$\dfrac{x^5}{x^3}$		
$\dfrac{x^3 y^2}{x y^2}$		
$\dfrac{x^5}{x}$		

a)   For each example, compare the exponents in the original form to the exponents in the simplified form. What do you notice?

b)   Simplify $\dfrac{20^{51}}{20^{12}}$ without writing the factored form. Describe what you did in detail.

MG-16.   Practice estimating square roots by writing your estimate as a mixed number and as a decimal, then using your calculator to check your estimate. Be sure to write your estimate before you use your calculator. Round your answers to the nearest hundredth (0.01). You should have three answers for each problem.

a) $\sqrt{45}$ b) $\sqrt{260}$

c) $\sqrt{650}$ d) $\sqrt{57}$

MG-17.   Howie and Steve are making cookies for themselves and some friends. The recipe they are using will make 48 cookies, but they only want to make 16 cookies. They have no trouble reducing the amounts of flour and sugar, but the original recipe calls for

$1\frac{3}{4}$ cups of butter. Help Howie and Steve determine how much butter they will need.

MG-18.   I am thinking of a number. If you multiply it by $\frac{1}{3}$ and then add 13, the result is 94. Write an equation and solve it to find my number.

MG-19.   Simplify the expression $5 + 2^2 \cdot 3 - 3.75(5 - 4)$.

MG-20.   Use subproblems to calculate the area of the figure at
          right. List each subproblem and show your work.

6 m

8 m

5 m

10 m

MG-21.   Graph each of the following equations on the same set of axes.

a) $y = \frac{4}{3}x - 3$ b) $y = -\frac{1}{3}x + 2$

MG-22.   Your teacher will lead a demonstration about the
          volume of cones.

r = 1.35

h = 11

a)   How are the radius and height of each cone
      related to the radius and height of each
      corresponding cylinder.

b)   Sketch the two cones in your notebook.
      Label the radius and height of each one.

r = 1.75

h = 8

c)   Estimate which cone you think will have the
      greater volume. Write "I think this one will
      have more volume" below the cone you
      believe has more volume.

d)   How many cones full of rice were needed to fill its corresponding cylinder?

e)   Based on your teacher's demonstration, describe how the volume of a cone
      compares to the volume of a cylinder of the same base and height.

f)   Find the volume of each cone.

MG-23.   On a separate sheet of paper, write the instructions for how to
          find the volume of the cone shown at right.

10 cm

3 cm

a)   Trade papers with your partner. Follow the instructions
      your partner wrote to find the volume of the cone.

b)   Let your partner know if the instructions were clear and
      easy to follow. Give suggestions for how the instructions
      could have been better.

MG-24.   Get a resource page from your teacher. Let each member of your study team calculate th
          data for one of the cones shown. If there are absent team members, divide the remaining
          work among those who are present. The first cone is shown below.

Cones	Scale Factor	Area of Circular Base	Ratio of Areas $\frac{New}{Original}$	Volume Cubic Units	Ratio of Volumes $\frac{New}{Original}$
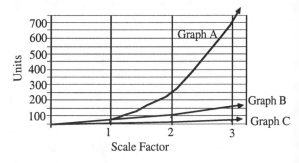	1	12.56 cm²	$\frac{12.56}{12.56}$	25.12 cm³	$\frac{25.12}{25.12} = \frac{1}{1}$

     a)   Complete each row of the table. Write the ratios twice, both as a decimal and as a
          ratio.

     b)   Share your results with your team so that all team members have a complete set of
          data. Check to make sure the data is correct.

     c)   Compare your results for the ratios of the area and volume to the Tool Kit entry in
          problem MG-14. Be sure your results are consistent with the basic relationships
          there.

MG-25.   Refer to the graph at right to
          answer the following questions.

     a)   Which graph represents
          the height of the different
          cones?

     b)   Which graph represents
          the area of the base of the
          different cones?

     c)   Which graph represents the volume of the different cones?

     d)   Explain how you determined your choices for parts (a), (b), and (c).

MG-26.

VOLUME OF A CONE

Every cone has a volume that is one-third the volume of the cylinder with the same base and height. To find the volume of a cone, use the same formula as the volume of a cylinder and divide by three. The formula for the volume of a cone of base area A and height h is:

$$V = \frac{A \cdot h}{3}$$

When the base of the cone is a circle of radius r, the formula is:

$$V = \frac{\pi r^2 h}{3} \quad \text{or} \quad \frac{1}{3}\pi r^2 h$$

Highlight the equation to calculate the volume of a cone in your Tool Kit.

MG-27.   Find the volume of a cone with a height of 8 feet and a radius of 5 feet. Draw a sketch and show your work.

MG-28.   Copy and complete the table.

Original Form	Factored Form	Simplified Form
$(5^2)^5$	$(5 \cdot 5)(5 \cdot 5)(5 \cdot 5)(5 \cdot 5)(5 \cdot 5)$	5^{10}
$(2^2)^4$		
$(3^7)^2$		
$(x^3)^5$		
$(x^3 y^2)^2$		

a)   For each example, compare the exponents in the original form to the exponent(s) in the simplified form. What do you notice?

b)   Simplify $(20^2)^{51}$ without writing the factored form. Describe in detail what you did.

MG-29. Sketch the prism at right on your paper.

a) Calculate the surface area and volume.

b) Suppose you wanted to know the surface area and volume of a prism with dimensions $\frac{1}{2}$ those of the prism at right. You could find the new surface area by writing the equation $\frac{1^2}{2^2} = \frac{\text{surface area}}{3312}$. Find the surface area of the new prism, then use a similar proportion to find its volume.

c) What would be the new surface area and volume if you reduced the original dimensions to $\frac{1}{3}$ the size of the original prism?

MG-30. The regular size Yummy Soup can has a rectangular label like the one shown at right.

a) Assuming that the label cannot overlap, find the diameter and radius of the can.

b) Find the dimensions of the label on the family size can if it is $\frac{7}{5}$ of the size of the regular size can.

c) Explain how to find the volume of any reduced figure without using volume formulas.

MG-31. Shante is painting a building with 33 identical offices. If she uses 14 gallons of paint for the first six offices, how much paint will she need to paint all 33 offices?

MG-32. Follow your teacher's directions for practicing mental math. Write the new strategy you learned.

G-33.　Read the rules below for Pair Up, the game you will be playing today. As you play, you must record each turn you take on your paper.

Pair Up
A game for two people.

Mathematical Purpose: To simplify expressions with exponents.

Object: To make card pairs by matching each problem with the simplified exponential expression.

Materials: Pair-Up cards: Problem Deck and Solution Deck

Scoring: One point for each correct match. Two points for each correct match if the card contains an asterisk. Card pairs with asterisks (rule cards) are worth two points because they use the laws of exponents.

How to Play the Game:
- Spread the solution cards face up in the shape of a rectangle..
- Designate Player One and Player Two.
- Player One draws a card from the deck, copies the problem on his or her paper, and simplifies it. Player One then finds the simplified solution card to match. Player One earns one point after Player Two verifies the cards match. If Player One's solution is incorrect, s/he loses his/her turn.
- Player Two may try using the same expression. If Player Two is successful, Player Two is awarded the point.
- Now it is Player Two's turn. Player Two repeats the same steps.

Ending the Game:　The game ends when all of the card pairs are gone. Whoever has the most points wins.

G-34.　After playing Pair Up, complete each question below.

a)　Record the scores for you and your partner.

b)　Who won?

c)　Locate the card pairs with asterisks and lay them out so that all players can view them. These pairs are the laws of exponents represented with symbols. Write a word sentence for each of these rules.

d)　Which exponent rules did you find most difficult?

G-35.

LAWS OF EXPONENTS

$$x^a \cdot x^b = x^{(a+b)} \qquad (x^a)^b = x^{ab} \qquad \frac{x^a}{x^b} = x^{(a-b)}$$

$$x^0 = 1 \qquad (x^a y^b)^c = x^{ac} y^{bc}$$

These rules hold if $x \neq 0$ and $y \neq 0$.

For each rule, there are three card pair examples in the game. Choose one example for each of the rules and copy it into your Tool Kit.

MG-36.   Use the laws of exponents to simplify the following problems.

a) $(x^2)(x^5)$ b) $x^7 \cdot x^5$ c) $y^8 \cdot y^6$ d) $y^7 \div y^4$

e) $\dfrac{x^3}{x^1}$ f) $x^3 \cdot x^4$ g) $m^{13} \cdot m^{14}$ h) $x^{32} \cdot x^{59}$

MG-37.   Donald has been taking care of his neighbor's cat every day for two weeks while the neighbor is on vacation. Donald is being paid $2 per day.

a)   How much did Donald make for the two weeks?

b)   The neighbor calls to say that the family wants to stay another two weeks and wants Donald to continue to take care of the cats. Donald agrees, but he wants to change the pay rate. He says, "Will you pay me 2¢ for the first day, 4¢ for the second day, 8¢ for the third day, and so on for the two weeks?" The neighbor agrees readily and thinks to herself, "Wow! What a great deal! I guess Donald didn't do too well in math." Is the neighbor right or does Donald know his math? Organize the information in a table to support your answer.

Day Number	Amount Earned	Total Earnings
1	$0.02	$0.02
2	$0.04	$0.06
3	$0.08	$0.14

c)   Copy and continue the table above to show Donald's earnings for the next 14 days. Use the data to make a graph. Scale your axes appropriately. Label the horizontal axis "Days" and the vertical axis "Total Amount Earned."

d)   Does your graph support your answer to part (b)? Explain why or why not.

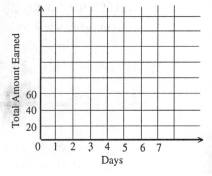

MG-38. Find the volume of the cone at right. You will need to use the Pythagorean Theorem to find the height. Show your work. (The answer is not 376.8 cubic centimeters.)

10 cm

6 cm

MG-39. The graph at right represents the number of books that are in each of several students' backpacks and how much each backpack weighs. Answer the following questions after studying the graph.

a) How many backpacks do you see represented on the graph?

b) Of all the backpacks graphed, which one <u>weighs</u> the median weight?

c) Of all the backpacks graphed, which one has the median <u>number of books</u> in it?

d) What is the mode for the weight?

e) What is the mode for the number of books?

f) Write a correlation for the scatter plot.

MG-40. Blanca is making a one-foot square ceramic tile for her art class. In the upper left corner she wants to put a design that is $\frac{1}{3}$-foot by $\frac{3}{4}$-foot. What is the area her design will cover? Draw a sketch of the entire tile and then shade the part that will contain her design.

MG-41. Complete the following Diamond Problems.

Product a)   b)   c)   d)   e)

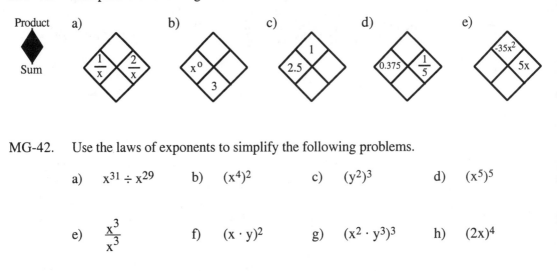

Sum

MG-42. Use the laws of exponents to simplify the following problems.

a) $x^{31} \div x^{29}$ b) $(x^4)^2$ c) $(y^2)^3$ d) $(x^5)^5$

e) $\dfrac{x^3}{x^3}$ f) $(x \cdot y)^2$ g) $(x^2 \cdot y^3)^3$ h) $(2x)^4$

MG-43. Below is a cone and two cylinders. All have the same radius. Use your knowledge of cones and cylinders to calculate mentally the volume of each cylinder.

a)   b)

Cone volume:
25 cubic cm

Cylinder A

Cylinder B

MG-44. Follow your teacher's example and complete the table for powers of 10.

a) In the table you have constructed, you should see a pattern. Use the pattern to decide how many zeros 10^7 will have. How many zeros will 10^{23} have?

b) How would you write 10^{-7}?

c) How would you tell someone to write 10^{50}? 10^{-50}? Do not actually write the numbers; just write a sentence telling someone how s/he would write them.

Powers of 10	Standard For
10^4	
10^3	
10^2	100
10^1	10
10^0	
10^{-1}	

MG-45. Multiply.

    a) $9.23 \cdot 10$ b) $9.23 \cdot 10^2$ c) $9.23 \cdot 10^3$ d) $9.23 \cdot 10^4$

    e)   Without computing, what do you think $9.23 \cdot 10^{10}$ would be?

    f)   Write a sentence describing in words what happens to the decimal point when you multiply a number by 10^4.

MG-46.   Predict where you think the decimal point will be after these factors are multiplied. Record your prediction. Use your calculator to check your answers. Organize your work in a table like the one below.

Factors	Prediction	Check
$78.659 \cdot 10^2$		
$346.387162 \cdot 10^5$		
$24.68931 \cdot 10^8$		

Describe where the decimal point of a number moves after multiplying the number by a power of 10 with a positive exponent.

MG-47.   Predict where you think the decimal point will be after these factors are multiplied. Use your calculator to check your answers. Organize your work in a table like the one below. Notice the negative exponents.

Factors	Prediction	Check
$3471 \cdot 10^{-3}$		
$689.32 \cdot 10^{-5}$		
$72187.65 \cdot 10^{-6}$		

Describe the decimal point movement when multiplying by a power of 10 with a negative exponent.

MG-48. Predict where you think the decimal point will move after these numbers are divided. Record your prediction. Use your calculator to check your answer. Organize your work in a table like the one shown.

Numbers	Prediction	Check
$3471 \div 10^3$		
$689.32 \div 10^5$		
$72187.65 \div 10^6$		

a) Compare your answers to those in problem MG-47.

b) Write a sentence or two explaining the relationship between multiplying a number by a negative powers of 10 and dividing by positive powers.

MG-49. Make a three-dimensional sketch of the product package that you and your team member will be enlarging and shrinking.

a) Measure your product package and include its dimensions on your sketch. If your product package is a rectangular prism, you will need to label the height and the length and width of its base. If it is a cylinder, you will need to label the height and the radius of its base.

b) Calculate the surface area and volume of your product package.

MG-50. Use the resource page provided by your teacher to do the exercises below.

a) Sketch two intersecting lines and mark the intersection. Name the geometric figure that marks the intersection of two lines.

b) Darken two different intersecting edges on the cube. Name the geometric figure that marks the intersection of two edges.

c) Find and darken a pair of parallel edges on the cube and shade the face that contains them.

d) Darken two parallel edges on the cube that are not part of the same face and sketch in the plane that contains them.

e) Darken a pair of edges on the cube that are **skew lines** (lines in three-dimensional space that do not lie in the same plane, do not intersect, and are not parallel).

f) Shade a pair of intersecting faces on the cube and darken the edge that marks the intersection. Sketch the dotted lines that indicate the line is infinite.

g) Shade three intersecting faces on the cube. Name the geometric figure that marks the intersection.

MG-51. Name the geometric figures formed by the intersection of:

a) two distinct lines.   b) two distinct planes.   c) three distinct planes.

MG-52. Angela bought a set of cylindrical canisters for her kitchen. The largest one, shown at right, has a diameter of seven inches and a height of 15 inches.

a) Sketch the canister and label its dimensions.

b) Calculate the volume of the canister.

MG-53. Inside the large canister from the previous problem is a smaller canister that is mathematically similar to the original. The smaller canister has $\frac{4}{5}$ the height and diameter of the large one.

a) Sketch and label the dimensions of the smaller canister.

b) Find the volume of the smaller canister.

MG-54. The Top Grade Gasoline station buys gasoline for $1.15 per gallon. The station used to sell 5000 gallons per day at $1.41 per gallon. The owner recently raised the price to $1.49 per gallon but now sells only 4000 gallons per day.

a) How has the price change affected Top Grade Gasoline's daily profits?

b) By what percentage did the total revenue from sales change?

MG-55. Solve for x.

a) $\frac{1}{2}(6x + 4) = 2x - 11$ b) $\frac{2}{3}x + 12 = x - 15$ c) $2\frac{1}{3}x + 1 = \frac{1}{3}x + 29$

MG-56.   Michael brought a bag of sand back from the
          seashore for Janessa's sandbox. On the way to
          the car, the bag developed a hole and he lost one-
          third of the sand. When he got home, he
          discovered he had lost an additional two-fifths of
          the sand. What was the total loss of sand?

MG-57.   Solve each inequality and sketch the graph of the solution on the number line.

a) $46 > \frac{2}{3}x + 32$ b) $13 - 3x \geq 25$

MG-58.   Find the product: $\frac{2}{3} \cdot \frac{3}{4} \cdot \frac{4}{5} \cdot \ldots \cdot \frac{99}{100}$.

MG-59.   Sketch the rectangular prism shown at
          right. Label the dimensions and calculate
          the surface area and volume. Show all
          your subproblems.

a)   Enlarge the dimensions by a factor of 100%. Sketch and label the enlarged prism
      Calculate the new surface area and volume. Show all your subproblems.

b)   Explain how you could have calculated the new surface area and volume without
      using the area and volume formulas.

c)   What is the percentage increase in surface area? What is the percentage increase i
      volume? Use a proportion to find out. Using your Tool Kit on percent increase
      might help you get started.

MG-60. With all the enlarging and reducing of things going on in class, Leigh had a dream that he shrunk his dog, Mantra, a large Malamute. In his dream, Mantra's new volume was 36,000 cubic centimeters.

a) Use a proportion to calculate the percent decrease in volume if Mantra's original volume was 182,250 cubic centimeters.

b) Calculate the volume of Leigh's backpack if its dimensions are 15 centimeters by 30 by 30 centimeters by 45 centimeters.

c) Will the shrunken dog fit in Leigh's backpack? Explain.

d) What would Mantra's volume be if her new dimensions were only $\frac{1}{9}$ of her original dimensions?

MG-61. Rink's favorite drink, Aloha Pineapple Juice, is packaged in a can like the one shown at right. Even after drinking it, he always feels thirsty. He wants the company to package the juice in a larger can.

a) If the company enlarges the dimensions of the can by a ratio of $\frac{4}{1}$, how much juice would the can hold? Show your work or explain how you got your answer.

b) Does it seem likely that the company will make a can that size? Explain.

MG-62. The label of the Aloha Pineapple Juice can is seven inches high and has an area of 140 square inches. What is the diameter of the can?

7 inches

MG-63. In a sentence, precisely describe the following numbers in words so that someone reading what you describe could write them without seeing all of the digits.

a) The mass of the sun is approximately 1,990,000,000,000,000,000,000,000,000,000 kg.

b) The mass of an electron is approximately 0.000000000000000000000000000000911 kg.

MG-64. Some scientists use very large and very small numbers. They have a simplified way of writing these numbers called **scientific notation**.

a) In scientific notation, the mass of the sun is approximately $1.99 \cdot 10^{30}$ kg. Compare this number to the one in MG-63 part (a). Explain what was done to write it in scientific notation.

b) The mass of an electron is approximately $9.11 \cdot 10^{-31}$ kg in scientific notation. Compare this number to the one in the previous problem part (b). Explain what was done to write it in scientific notation. In particular, what does the negative exponent mean?

MG-65.

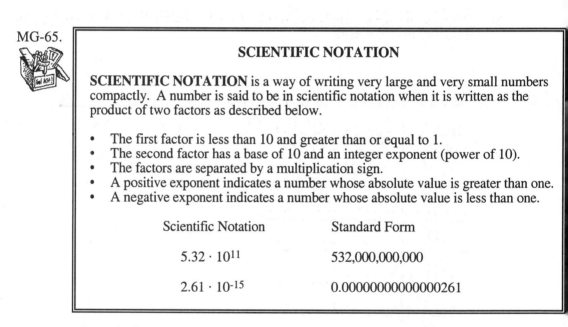

SCIENTIFIC NOTATION

SCIENTIFIC NOTATION is a way of writing very large and very small numbers compactly. A number is said to be in scientific notation when it is written as the product of two factors as described below.

- The first factor is less than 10 and greater than or equal to 1.
- The second factor has a base of 10 and an integer exponent (power of 10).
- The factors are separated by a multiplication sign.
- A positive exponent indicates a number whose absolute value is greater than one.
- A negative exponent indicates a number whose absolute value is less than one.

Scientific Notation	Standard Form
$5.32 \cdot 10^{11}$	532,000,000,000
$2.61 \cdot 10^{-15}$	0.00000000000000261

Write the following numbers in scientific notation and record them in your Tool Kit to the right of the double-lined box.

a) 370,000,000

b) 0.0000000000076

MG-66. Lani bought ice cream to eat on her way home. She remembered that she needed to buy fish food, so she set the cone in a cup holder in her car and went back into the store. It took longer than she thought it would, and by the time she got back to her car, the ice cream had melted completely.

Show your work for each problem below.

a) Calculate the volume of the ice cream "scoop" (the cylinder).

b) Calculate the volume of the cone.

c) Did the melted ice cream overflow the cone or is it all in the cone? Why?

d) What minimum cone height would hold all the ice cream? Write an equation or use a Guess and Check table.

MG-67. Copy and complete the chart of these cubed fractions.

Exponent Form	Factored Form	Standard Form
$\left(\frac{1}{2}\right)^3$	$\frac{1}{2} \cdot \frac{1}{2} \cdot \frac{1}{2}$	$\frac{1}{8}$
$\left(\frac{1}{3}\right)^3$		
$\left(\frac{1}{4}\right)^3$		
$\left(\frac{1}{5}\right)^3$		
$\left(\frac{2}{3}\right)^3$		
$\left(\frac{3}{4}\right)^3$		
$\left(\frac{2}{5}\right)^3$		
$\left(\frac{4}{5}\right)^3$		

MG-68. In Payne's class, seven students had three siblings, six students had two siblings, nine students had one sibling, and three students had no siblings. What is the mean number of siblings for students in Payne's class?

MG-69. The difference $\dfrac{3^2 + 7}{4} - \dfrac{8 - 4^2}{2}$ is:

(A) 8 (B) -4 (C) 0 (D) -5

MG-70. Simplify.

a) -3 + 0.05   b) -7 + (-2.8)   c) 7 + (-10.6)   d) -5.8 + 2

MG-71. Determine which of the quantities below is larger. Do the problem in your head, without a pencil or paper. Describe your method in detail.

Which is larger: $\dfrac{1}{3} + \dfrac{2}{4} + \dfrac{2}{5} + \dfrac{5}{11}$ or 2?

MG-72. Margy thought that her family's cookie canister was too small, so she decided to buy a new one. She told her son Chris that the canisters were similar. Margy asked Chris to find the percent increase in volume of the new canister. Solve this problem for Chris.

a) Use a proportion to find the height in inches of the larger cookie canister. Round your answer to the nearest tenth.

b) Calculate the volume of both canisters and the percentage the volume increased.

MG-73.   **Cracker Snacks**

The Clifford Snack Company produces cracker
canisters. Their snack-size canisters are similar to
full-size canisters but have been reduced by a scale
factor of $\frac{2}{5}$. Use the dimensions of the full-size
canisters to calculate the surface area and volume
of both the full-size and the snack-size canisters.

a)   Full-size cracker canisters come in shapes and
sizes like the equilateral triangular prism,
square-based prism, and cylinder shown at
right. Calculate the surface area and the
volume of each full-size cracker canister.

b)   Sketch the snack-size canisters and record the new dimensions if they have been
reduced by a factor of $\frac{2}{5}$. Calculate the surface area and volume of each of the
snack-size canisters.

MG-74.   Copy and complete the table below.

Standard Form	Scientific Notation
568,000,000,000,000,000,000,000,000	
	$1.11 \cdot 10^{-15}$
30,000,000,000,000	
99,810,000,000,000,000,000,000	
	$4.72 \cdot 10^{-9}$
	$1.2 \cdot 10^{2}$
0.000000000000000034	

MG-75.   Use the laws of exponents to simplify the following problems.

a) $x^4 \div x^3$ b) $(x^3)^4$ c) $(2y^2)^3$ d) $(x^2)^4$

e) $\dfrac{x^2}{x^{-3}}$ f) $(xy^2)^2$ g) $(x^2y^2)^4$ h) $(2x)^3$

MG-76. Solve the following equations.

a) $x + \frac{3}{4} = 6\frac{5}{6}$

b) $\frac{1}{2}x + \frac{3}{4} = 1$

MG-77. Simplify.

a) $\frac{3}{4} \cdot 5\frac{1}{5}$

b) $\frac{11}{4} \cdot -2\frac{1}{3}$

c) $-\frac{1}{3} \div \frac{2}{5}$

d) $\frac{1}{8} \cdot (0.6)$

e) $\frac{-112}{2} \cdot \frac{1}{6}$

f) $-2\frac{2}{3} + \frac{1}{7}$

MG-78. First-place trophies cost $8.25 each. What is the total cost of a first-place trophy if there is a tax of 8%?

MG-79. What percent of 25 is 13? Show your work.

MG-80. Darrel and Rosemary built their new home in the shape of the diagram below. (All of the measurements are in feet.)

a) Find the total area of their home. Be sure to show all of your subproblems.

b) Find the area of their circular pool.

c) If the dimensions of their lot are 150 feet by 175 feet, what is its perimeter?

d) What is the area available for a driveway, walkways, and landscaping?

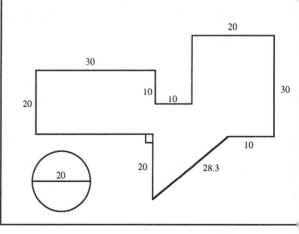

MG-81. Take out the product package that your team has selected. Use the measurements and product sketches to help you continue.

a) Discuss with your study team members the scale factor you want to use to enlarge the size of your product package and the scale factor you want to use to reduce the size of your product package. Record the scale factors you have chosen.

b) Decide with your team members who will construct the enlarged product package and who will construct the reduced product package. Record your decision.

c) For your package, make a sketch of the "new" product package. Be sure to include the new dimensions.

d) For your package, calculate the surface area of your "new" product package and write the ratio of the new surface area to the original surface area. Simplify your ratio.

e) For your package, calculate the volume of your "new" product package and write the ratio of the new volume to the original volume. Simplify your ratio.

f) Have your other team members check your calculations.

g) Obtain the materials you will need to build your "new" product package.

h) Use your measurements from MG-49 to make a template for your "new" product package. You may need to use several sheets of tag board depending on your enlargement factor.

i) Carefully cut out the template and fold or glue the pieces together.

j) Use construction paper and crayons or markers to draw the label for your "new" product package. Be sure your label is also drawn to scale.

MG-82. Match each expression below with its correct answer.

a) $2 \cdot 2 \cdot 2$ 4

b) x^4 $2^2 \cdot 3^2$

c) $5h$ $3x$

d) 36 $x \cdot x \cdot x \cdot x$

e) $\sqrt{16}$ 8

f) $x + x + x$ $5 \cdot h$

MG-83.   Simplify each of the following expressions.

a) $2^2 + 3^2$

b) $7^2 \cdot 7 \cdot 7$

c) $4^2 + 5^2$

d) $8^2 + 7^2$

e) $(2^2 + 6)^2$

f) $3^2 + 5^2$

g) $x - x$

h) $3 \cdot 3 \div 3$

i) $4x + x - 2x$

MG-84.   Simplify the following expression. Show each step and explain in words what you did.

$$\frac{3 - 2(5 - 1) + 3}{9 - 7}$$

MG-85.   Juan found that 20 new pencils weigh 12 ounces. How much will 50 new pencils weigh? Set up a proportion and solve it.

MG-86.   The perimeter of this triangle is 47 cm. Solve for x and compute the length of each side. Show your equation.

$2x + 3$ $x + 7$ $4x + 2$

MG-87.   Bethany just bought an amazing Cube-o-saurus. The package says, "Soak in water overnight and the cube-o-saurus will get an amazing eight times larger." The cube-shaped dinosaur starts out about one centimeter on a side. Bethany is looking forward to seeing the 8-centimeter long creature. The next morning she finds the Cube-o-saurus is the same shape and only 2 centimeters long, 2 centimeters tall, and 2 centimeters wide. Was the Cube-o-saurus falsely advertised? Is the new shape eight times larger?

MG-88.   Ned and his family are at a restaurant for dinner. The bill is $87 and they want to leave a tip of 15% of the bill. Set up a proportion and solve it to find how much of a tip Ned's family should leave.

MG-89.   Answer the comparison questions below.

   a)   How many times larger is $3 \cdot 3 \cdot 3$ than $3 + 3 + 3$?

   b)   How many times larger is $\frac{1}{3} + \frac{1}{3} + \frac{1}{3}$ than $\frac{1}{3} \cdot \frac{1}{3} \cdot \frac{1}{3}$?

MG-90.   Which is larger: 2^5 or 5^2 ? Explain how you know.

MG-91.   Follow your teacher's instructions for practicing mental math.

MG-92.   How much larger is $\frac{1}{2} + \frac{1}{2} + \frac{1}{2}$ than $\frac{1}{2} \cdot \frac{1}{2} \cdot \frac{1}{2}$?

MG-93.   Angela needed $\frac{1}{8}$ of a piece of material that was $\frac{2}{3}$ of a yard long. What was the length of her piece?

MG-94.   A bacteria cell splits in half to form two cells.
          Eventually those two cells will grow and then split in
          half to form four cells. This process is repeated over
          and over again every twenty minutes, three times
          every hour.

   a)   Draw a sketch of each generation for the first
          four splits. Copy the table below to help you
          record the number of cells at each generation.

Time	0:20	0:40	1:00	1:20	1:40	2:00
Splits	1	2	3	4	5	6
Total Cells	2	4				
Total Cells (exponential form)	2^1	2^2				

   b)   Extend your table to Time = 4:00 and complete it. You do not have to draw the
          generations.

Time						
Splits						
Total Cells						
Total Cells (exponential form)						

>>Problem continues on the next page.>>

c)   What exponential pattern do you notice?

d)   By the end of the eleventh hour, how many cells will there be? Write your answer scientific notation.

e)   After 24 hours, how many cells will there be? Use your calculator to find the answer, but remember that for very large numbers your calculator will display scientific notation. Many calculators show scientific notation as 1.3^{03} meaning $1.3 \cdot 10^3 = 1300$. Rewrite the calculator display for the number of cells at 24 hour in proper scientific notation and in standard form.

MG-95.   When Jason arrives for his shift as a toll taker for the Pacific Bridge, he finds that there are 44 dollars in his cash drawer. Cars begin coming through the toll booth, and soon he is very busy. After half an hour, Jason has a spare moment and counts the money in his drawer. He finds that the drawer contains $178.

a)   Since each car pays $2 to cross the bridge, determine how many cars have come by his booth during his shift.

b)   At the same rate, how many cars will come by Jason's booth during his six-hour shift?

MG-96.   What is the range of the data set 114, 728, 364, 487, 546, 1478, 287, 98, 821 ?

(A) 1380   (B) 1478   (C) 1191   (D) 547

MG-97.   Complete the following Diamond Problems.

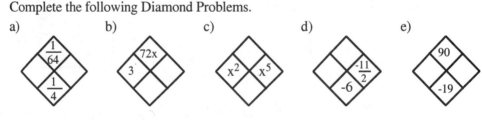

MG-98.   Caylan used a third of a tank of gas to drive to the ocean. On her way to take her cousin home, she used a fourth of a tank. If her tank holds 18 gallons and she gets 30 miles per gallon, how many more miles can she drive?

MG-99. **Chapter Summary** As you finish a chapter, you
need to reflect on how well you know the material.
Find a problem in the chapter that represents what
you have learned each of the following topics. Copy
the problem and show the correct solution for the
problem. Explain why you selected the problem.

- Volume and surface area of a prism

- Volume of a cone

- Laws of exponents

- Scientific notation

MG-100. **Course Summary** Your teacher will assign each team a chapter to summarize.

a)   For the chapter assigned to you, list the objectives from the front of the chapter.
Restate them in your own words.

b)   List the Tool Kit entries from the end of the chapter.

c)   With your team, select five problems from the chapter that you think best represent
the objectives and the Tool Kit.

d)   Write out the solutions for the problems.

e)   Prepare a poster to present to the rest of the class that shows the chapter objectives
(in your words), the Tool Kit list, and the five problems with their solutions. Be
ready to explain why you chose those particular problems and how they illustrate
important ideas from the course.

MG-101.   Your job is to create some new problems for the final exam. Your teacher will assign your team another chapter. Use the five problems selected for that chapter as a basis for writing the new problems. Sometimes you can do this by just changing some numbers Sometimes you will need to change the whole problem. Two examples are given below

Find the area.

Old: New:

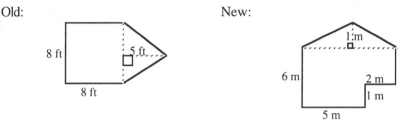

Solve the equation.

Old: $5(x - 3) = -7x + 18$ New: $-3(x - 5) = -2x + 10$

a)   With your team, write one different problem that is similar to each of the five posted problems.

b)   Solve each of the problems your team wrote.

MG-102.   Find the surface area of the hexagonal prism shown at right. Dividing the hexagon into smaller parts and using subproblems will help.

a)   Find the area of the hexagonal bases by answering parts (i) through (iii). The two obtuse triangles are congruent and the region in the middle is a rectangle.

   i)   Find the area of the four congruent triangles.

   ii)   Find the area of the two congruent rectangles.

   iii) Find the area of the hexagonal bases.

b)   Find the area of the lateral faces by answering parts (i) and (ii).

   i)   What are the dimensions of the lateral faces?

   ii)   Write an equation to find the total area of the lateral faces.

c)   Write an equation that gives the total surface area.

d)   How could you have used other subproblems to find the area of the hexagonal bases?

G-103. Light travels faster than sound. That is why you see lightning before you hear thunder during a thunder storm. The amount of time that passes between seeing the flash of lightning and hearing the thunder can actually tell you how far away the storm is. For example, if you see lightning and then hear thunder 10 seconds later, the lightning was about two miles away.

a) Copy and complete the table below for other times and distances, then graph the information. Scale your axes as shown below.
The x-values are the times in seconds between seeing the lightning and hearing the thunder. The y-values are the distances away (in miles) the lightning is.

x (time in seconds)	5	15	40			5n
y (distance in miles)	1	3		4	$4\frac{1}{2}$	

b) How could you use your graph to find how far away a storm is if the time lapse is $2\frac{1}{2}$ seconds?

c) If it took 25 seconds to hear the thunder, how far away is the lightning?

d) If you were 12 miles away from the storm, about how long would it take you to hear the thunder after seeing the lightning flash?

e) Why does it make sense that the graph goes through the point (0, 0)?

G-104. A group of mountain climbers hears thunder 30 seconds after they see the lightning.

a) About how far are the climbers from the storm?

b) Two minutes later the mountain climbers hear thunder again, but now they hear the thunder 20 seconds after they see the lightning. Now how far are they from the storm?

c) How fast is the storm traveling?

MG-105. Cheryl and Jeremy are playing a game in which they use two dice. They must subtract the numbers on each die. The number rolled on the second die is subtracted from the number rolled on the first die. Copy and complete the chart showing all of the possible differences.

a) What is the probability that Cheryl will roll a difference of 2 or 0?

b) It is now Jeremy's turn. What is the probability that he will roll a difference of 4 or -5?

c) What is the probability that Cheryl or Jeremy will roll a difference of zero?

d) What is the probability that Cheryl or Jeremy will roll a difference that is greater than 5?

Differences of Two Dice

First Die

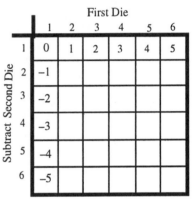

		1	2	3	4	5	6
Subtract Second Die	1	0	1	2	3	4	5
	2	-1					
	3	-2					
	4	-3					
	5	-4					
	6	-5					

MG-106. Use the laws of exponents to simplify each expression.

a) $x^5 \cdot x^4$

b) $\dfrac{n^{12}}{n^3}$

c) $(y)(3y^2)$

d) $(x^3)^2$

e) $\dfrac{x^4}{x^1}$

f) $\dfrac{y^2 x^6}{xy}$

g) $\dfrac{n^{-2}}{n^5}$

h) $(2x^3)^3$

MG-107. There are 36 green gumballs, 18 red gumballs, 22 white gumballs, 30 purple gumballs, and 14 blue gumballs in the gumball machine. Answer the following questions using percentages. Make sure you show your work.

a) What is the probability of getting a purple gumball?

b) What is the probability of getting either a purple or a white gumball?

c) What is the probability of not getting a greengum ball?

CHAPTER 1(

MG-108. **What We Have Done in This Chapter**

Below is a list of the Tool Kit entries from this chapter.

- MG-14   Ratios of Dimensional Change
- MG-26   Volume of a Cone
- MG-35   Laws of Exponents
- MG-65   Scientific Notation

Review all the entries and read the notes you made in your Tool Kit. Make a list of any questions, terms, or notes you do not understand. Ask your partner or study team members for help. If anything is still unclear, ask your teacher.

Appendix A
Making the Order of Operations Formal: MATHEMATICAL NAMES

INTRODUCTION

So far in this book, we have tried to help you understand the ideas behind what you are doing. Now is the time to give the formal names to what you already understand, so that when someone asks you for a reason for your actions, you can give them a name for your reason—rather like being able to name a period in history (early Roman Empire) or a scientific effect (evaporation). Therefore, much of this Interlude will be telling rather than asking you to work on problems. Then, after we have told you the names that mathematicians give certain ideas, we will give you some examples and then more problems for practice.

BACKGROUND

Mathematicians did not just sit down one day many years ago and make up the properties we will be talking about. Each of these properties comes from working with the whole numbers (0, 1, 2, 3, ...) and seeing the rules which always work for them. One such rule is $A \cdot B = B \cdot A$ for any two natural numbers A and B. This is not a surprise to you. You have known for a long time that, for example, $3 \cdot 4 = 4 \cdot 3$. What is different, however, is that many years ago, people studying algebra decided it was important to give this rule a name (the Commutative Property) and—this is the important part—to say that this rule works for <u>all</u> numbers. We use this property when we work with any kind of numbers: positive, negative, fractions, and even some kinds of numbers you may not know yet, like complex numbers. But once you have learned these rules and learned how to use them, you can be sure that they will always work. So the rule we gave earlier ($A \cdot B = B \cdot A$) is true even if A and B are these other kinds of numbers.

THE PROPERTIES OF ARITHMETIC OPERATIONS AND THEIR FORMAL NAMES

Additive Identity This is just the number zero (0). The name comes from the fact that when you add zero to any number, you get the same number you started with. That is, $x + 0 = x$ for any number x. This property is actually how the additive identity is defined: z is the additive identity if, for every number x, $z + x = x + z = x$. But you know it is the number zero.

Additive Inverse An inverse operation in general is about undoing. Suppose you have the number 4 and want to add something to it to get zero (the additive identity). The number you would have to add would be -4. So we say that -4 is the additive inverse of 4. Similarly, the additive inverse of -3 is 3 since $(-3) + 3 = 0$. So, just like the previous definition, we say that for any number x, we get its additive inverse y if $x + y = y + x = 0$.

Multiplicative Identity The number one (1). Just as adding the additive identity to a number does not change it, multiplying a number by the multiplicative identity does not change that number. So w is the multiplicative identity if, for every number x, $w \cdot x = x \cdot w = x$.

Multiplicative Inverse Suppose you have the number 4 and want to multiply it by something to get 1 (the multiplicative identity). You would have to multiply by $\frac{1}{4}$. So we say $\frac{1}{4}$ is the multiplicative inverse of 4. Similarly, the multiplicative inverse of $\frac{1}{8}$ is 8 since $8 \cdot \frac{1}{8} = 1$. Formally, y is the multiplicative inverse of x if $x \cdot y = y \cdot x = 1$. An important fact to know is that zero does not have a multiplicative inverse, but it is the only number which does not.

Distributive Property You have worked with this property a lot so far, and it is enormously important in algebra where you will need it almost every day. It relates addition and multiplication and says that $x \cdot (y + z) = x \cdot y + x \cdot z$. Usually you would just write $x(y + z) = xy + xz$, but we p in the multiplication signs to emphasize the multiplicative aspects of this property.

Commutative Property We referred to the commutative property above. It simply says that the order in which you add or multiply does not matter. That is, for any two numbers x and y, it is tru that $x + y = y + x$ and $x \cdot y = y \cdot x$. Technically, there are two properties here: the commutative property of addition and the commutative property of multiplication. We will refer to both of them under the single name, "Commutative Property."

Associative Property This is one property that has probably never occurred to you ever to doubt. It says that if you have three numbers to add (or to multiply), if you add the first two and then add the sum to the third, you get the same answer as if you add the second and third and then add that sum to the first. Here it is in symbolic form remembering that we do operations inside of parentheses first, $(x + y) + z = x + (y + z)$ and $(x \cdot y) \cdot z = x \cdot (y \cdot z)$ or, if we write it without the multiplication symbol, $(xy)z = x(yz)$. So, for example, $(3 + 4) + 5 = 7 + 5 = 12$, which is also the answer of $3 + (4 + 5) = 3 + 9$. Again, technically, there are two properties here: the associative property of addition and the associative property of multiplication. We will refer to both of them under the single name, "Associative Property."

EXAMPLES

Example 1. Find $20 \cdot 12$. We know that $12 = 10 + 2$, so by the Distributive Property, we know that $20 \cdot 12 = 20 \cdot (10 + 2) = 20 \cdot 10 + 20 \cdot 2 = 200 + 40 = 240$.

Example 2. Simplify $2x + 4 + 7x$. By the Commutative Property, we know that $4 + 7x = 7x +$ Now the problem becomes $2x + 7x + 4$. Using the usual order of operations, we solve this as $(2x + 7x) + 4$. Using the Distributive Property, $(2 + 7)x + 4 = 9x + 4$

Example 3. Show that $\frac{3}{4}$ and $\frac{24}{32}$ represent the same number. Using the Multiplicative Identity, $\frac{3}{4} \cdot 1 = \frac{3}{4}$. But when we write 1 as the Giant **1**, $\frac{8}{8}$, we see that $\frac{3}{4} \cdot \frac{8}{8} = \frac{24}{32}$. Thus, $\frac{3}{4} = \frac{24}{32}$.

PROBLEMS

MN-1.   Name the rule that allows us to do each of the following operations.

a) $4 + (5 + (-5)) = (4 + 5) + -5$ b) $5 \cdot 3 = 3 \cdot 5$

c) $3(x + 5) = 3x + 3 \cdot 5$ d) $14 + (-3) = -3 + 14$

e) $5 \cdot \dfrac{1}{5} = 1$ f) $\dfrac{2}{3} \cdot \dfrac{1}{6} = \dfrac{1}{6} \cdot \dfrac{2}{3}$

g) $x + 7z = 7z + x$ h) $13 + 0 = 13 + (-10 + 10)$

i) $7(x + yz) = 7x + 7yz$ j) $(z - w) \cdot 8 = 8 \cdot (z - w)$

k) $t + 0 = t$

MN-2.   Name the operation that allows us to do $1 \cdot 7 = 7 \cdot 1$.

(A) Multiplicative Inverse   (B) Distributive Property

(C) Commutative Property   (D) Additive Identity

MN-3.   Name the operation that allows us to do $1 \cdot 7 = 7$.

(A) Multiplicative Identity   (B) Distributive Property

(C) Commutative Property   (D) Additive Identity

MN-4.   Name the operation that allows us to do $3 + (4 + 5) = 3 + (5 + 4)$.

(A) Multiplicative Identity   (B) Associative Property

(C) Distributive Property   (D) Commutative Property

MN-5.   Name the operation that allows us to do $3 + (4 + 5) = (3 + 4) + 5$.

(A) Multiplicative Identity   (B) Associative Property

(C) Distributive Property   (D) Commutative Property

MN-6. Name the operation that allows us to do $-3 + 0 = -3$.

(A) Additive Identity   (B) Additive Inverse

(C) Distributive Property   (D) Associative Property

MN-7. Name the operation that allows us to do $-3 + 0 = -3 + (-6 + 6)$.

(A) Additive Identity   (B) Additive Inverse

(C) Distributive Property   (D) Associative Property

WHY A NEGATIVE TIMES A NEGATIVE IS A POSITIVE

Earlier in the course we gave an argument of why a negative integer times a negative integer is a positive integer which was primarily based on the idea that multiplying, say, $(-3) \cdot (-5)$ could be thought of as taking away 5 of the negative tiles and doing it 3 times. While most students come away from this demonstration knowing what the rule is and having a good idea why it works, the argument is more of a teaching device than a formal proof. Now, however, with the formal propertie we introduced above, we can give a complete and formal demonstration of this fact.

The central idea in our proof uses the distributive property and the additive identity. We give two arguments which are actually exactly the same except that one is a purely formal proof which really uses algebra while the other one just uses a particular pair of numbers x and y. Reading over this proof will probably be difficult for most students, but if you think you might want to be a mathematician someday, it is never too early to get started. It will probably be easier if you start witl the proof for Statement 1 that involves numbers. Then go to the more general one that uses variable

Statement 1 **If x is a positive number and y is a negative number, then xy is negative.**

We assume everyone knows three facts:
- If x and z are positive numbers, then their product is a positive number.
- The additive inverse of a positive number is negative and the additive inverse of a negative numbe is positive.
- If x is any number, then $x \cdot 0 = 0$.

Reasons that Statement 1 is true using a particular pair of numbers.

Suppose $x = 5$ and $y = -3$. Then the additive inverse of y is 3 since $(-3) + 3 = 0$. Now see what happens when we multiply $5 \cdot ((-3) + 3)$. We are going to treat $5 \cdot (-3)$ as an unknown and get information about it.

By the Distributive Property, we know that $5 \cdot ((-3) + 3) = 5 \cdot (-3) + 5 \cdot 3$. However, we also know that $5 \cdot ((-3) + 3) = 5 \cdot 0 = 0$. (Recall we assumed that $x \cdot 0 = 0$ for any number x.)
Therefore, the two products $5 \cdot (-3)$ and $5 \cdot 3$ are additive inverses since they add up to 0. But earlier we agreed that since 5 and 3 are positive, we know their product is positive. So their additive inverse—here $5 \cdot (-3)$—must be negative. So, at least for these two numbers with different signs, the product is negative.

Reasons that Statement 1 is true using algebra.

As stated, we assume that x is positive and y is negative. The additive inverse of y is $(-y)$, which we know is positive. Now see what happens when we multiply $x \cdot (y + (-y))$. We are going to treat $x \cdot y$ as an unknown and get information about it.

By the Distributive Property, we know that $x \cdot (y + (-y)) = x \cdot y + x \cdot (-y)$. However, we also know that $x \cdot (y + (-y)) = x \cdot 0 = 0$. Therefore, the two products $x \cdot y$ and $x \cdot (-y)$ are additive inverses since they add up to 0. But earlier we agreed that since x and $(-y)$ are positive, we know their product is positive. So their additive inverse—here $x \cdot y$—must be negative. Thus for any two numbers x and y, with x positive and y negative, their product is negative.

Now (at last) we are ready to show that a negative times a negative is a positive.

Statement 2 If x and y are negative numbers, then xy is positive.

Reasons that Statement 2 is true using a particular pair of numbers.

Suppose $x = -5$ and $y = -4$. Then the additive inverse of y is 4 since $(-4) + 4 = 0$. Now see what happens when we multiply $(-5) \cdot ((-4) + 4)$.

By the Distributive Property, we know that $(-5) \cdot ((-4) + 4) = (-5) \cdot (-4) + (-5) \cdot 4$. However, we also know that $(-5) \cdot ((-4) + 4) = 5 \cdot 0 = 0$. Therefore, the two products $(-5) \cdot (-4)$ and $(-5) \cdot 4$ are additive inverses since they add up to 0. But since (-5) is negative and 4 is positive, by what we learned from Statement 1, we know their product is negative. So their additive inverse—here $(-5) \cdot (-4)$—must be positive. So, at least for these two numbers with negative signs, their product is positive.

Reasons that Statement 2 is true using algebra.

As stated, we assume that x and y are both negative. The additive inverse of y is $(-y)$, which we know is positive. Now see what happens when we multiply $x \cdot (y + (-y))$.

Again, by the Distributive Property, we know that $x \cdot (y + (-y)) = x \cdot y + x \cdot (-y)$. However, we also know that $x \cdot (y + (-y)) = x \cdot 0 = 0$. Therefore, the two products $x \cdot y$ and $x \cdot (-y)$ are additive inverses since they add up to 0. But since x is negative and $(-y)$ is positive, by what we learned from Statement 1, we know their product is negative. So their additive inverse—here $x \cdot y$—must be positive. Thus for any two negative numbers x and y, their product is positive.

PROBLEM

MN-8.   In what we just did, we assumed that you knew that $x \cdot 0 = 0$ for any x. Actually, you can prove this statement, too, using the Distributive Property and the Additive Identity. As a hint, multiply the statement $1 + 0 = 1$ on both sides by x and see what happens.

Appendix B
Here are Constructions: COMPASS CONSTRUCTION

HC-1.   Today you will use a compass and straightedge to construct geometric figures. A straightedge is a line segment maker; a compass is a circle maker.

a)   Use a paper clip as a compass to make some circles. You may choose to use two pencils, one to draw and one to anchor the center of the circle. A push pin also works well to hold the center in place.

b)   Use one loop of the paper clip at a time to make two different circles with the same center. These are called **concentric** circles.

c)   Now use the plastic grid compass provided by your teacher (or the kind of compass your teacher specifies) in a similar manner and make some circles.

d)   Make four concentric circles using the plastic grid or other compass.

HC-2.   Toward the bottom edge of a new sheet of paper, make a line that is about the same length as the one below and label point A near the left part of the line.

a)   Center your compass on point A and use it to make a "slash" across the line the same distance from A as shown above. Find the point where the slash mark intersects the line and label it point B. This slash mark is a little piece of a whole circle. It is called an **arc**.

>> **Problem continues on next page.>>**

b) Next we will make an equilateral triangle. Start with your compass still centered at point A and mark an arc the length of line segment AB ($\overline{AB}$) above the center of the line as shown in the drawing.

c) Center the compass at point B. Use the same length and make another arc that intersects the one from part (b). Label the point of intersection C, as shown in the diagram.

C

d) Use your straightedge to draw $\overline{AC}$ and $\overline{BC}$ to make ΔABC. What kind of triangle is this?

A   B

HC-3.   Follow the steps below to construct ΔJKL.

a) Start by drawing a long line. Mark and label a line $\overline{JK}$ as you did $\overline{AB}$ in the previous problem.

b) Now center your compass at point J and choose any length that is more than half of the length of $\overline{JK}$ and not the same as $\overline{JK}$. Make two arcs above the center of the line segments from K, as you did in the previous problem.

c) Label the point of intersection L. Use your straightedge to draw $\overline{JL}$ and $\overline{JK}$ to complete the triangle.

d) What kind of triangle is this?

HC-4.   Next we will construct an **angle bisector**.

a) Draw an angle and label its vertex Q.

b) With the center of your compass at the vertex, draw an arc that intersects both sides (rays) of your angle and label the intersection points P and R respectively.

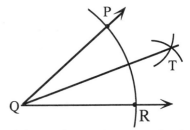

c) Center your compass at point P and make an arc mark out beyond your arc but in the interior of the angle.

d) Repeat part (c) from point R to intersect the first mark you made. Label this point T.

e) Line up the intersection of the two arc marks (point T) and the vertex and draw the angle bisector from Q through T.

HC-5.   In this problem we will construct a **perpendicular bisector** of a segment. Start with a line segment and label its endpoints, S and T.

S   T

a)   A perpendicular line makes right angles with another line. What is a bisector?

b)   Center your compass at point S and then at point T and make two pairs of crossing arcs as you did in problems HC-2 and HC-3, one above and the other below the line segment.

c)   Draw a line connecting the two pairs of crossing arcs. This line is the perpendicular bisector of the line segment $\overline{ST}$.

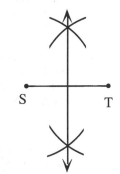

d)   Mark the point where the perpendicular bisector intersects $\overline{ST}$. Label it M and draw in the right angle box. Point M is the **midpoint** of $\overline{ST}$.

HC-6.   Use your compass to draw a circle.

a)   Mark a point A on the circle and center your compass at point A. Using a length the same as the radius, mark point B.

b)   Continue around the circle using the length of the radius and marking C, D, E, and F.

c)   Now carefully draw $\overline{AB}$, $\overline{BC}$, $\overline{CD}$, $\overline{DE}$, $\overline{EF}$, and $\overline{FA}$. Each of these is a **chord** in the circle.

d)   What geometric figure is created by the chords?

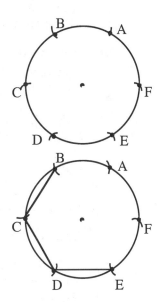

HC-7.   Construct a circle with the same six markings as in problem HC-6. Connect three of the points with chords so that an equilateral triangle is formed.

HC-8. Construct a circle with the same six markings as in problem HC-5. We are going to make a twelve-sided figure, a **dodecagon**.

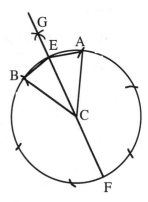

a) Draw ∠ACB with its vertex at the center of the circle. This is called a **central angle**.

b) Construct the angle bisector of ∠ACB. Draw the chords from points A and B to the point where the angle bisector intersects the circle (point E).

c) You do not need to draw the whole bisector. The important points are E and F, where the bisector crosses the circle and bisects the two arcs. What is the special name for $\overline{EF}$?

d) Use the method from part (c) to bisect the other arcs and draw a regular dodecagon.

HC-9. Start again with a circle. This time we will construct a square.

a) Draw a diameter $\overline{EF}$.

b) Construct the perpendicular bisector of the diameter.

c) Mark the points B and D where the perpendicular bisector intersects the circle.

d) Use your straightedge to connect the four points B, D, E, and F to make a square.

HC-10. Start with a construction like the one you did in problem HC-9. Now construct an octagon by using the same method as you used in problem HC-8, where you got twelve sides after starting with six sides.

HC-11. How could you use what you did in problem HC-10 to construct a 16-sided figure? Make that 16-sided figure now. You may want to start with a larger circle.

HC-12. In one circle, construct a triangle, a hexagon, and a dodecagon.

HC-13. In one circle, construct a square, an octagon, and a dodecagon.

HC-14.   Use the construction methods you have learned so far and your straightedge to connect
          points to make the following figures. Use a large circle on a whole sheet of paper to start
          each.

     a)   Construct a pattern like the one below in a larger size.

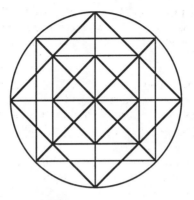

     b)   Construct a pattern like the one below in a larger size.

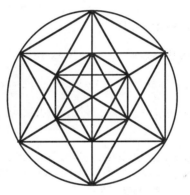

     c)   Shade one or both of your constructions in parts (a) or (b) to make a symmetric
           design.

HC-15.   Select one (or more) of the following designs to construct in a larger size. All of the construction makings have been erased, so you will need to do some problem solving to decide how these designs were constructed using only the constructions you have learned.

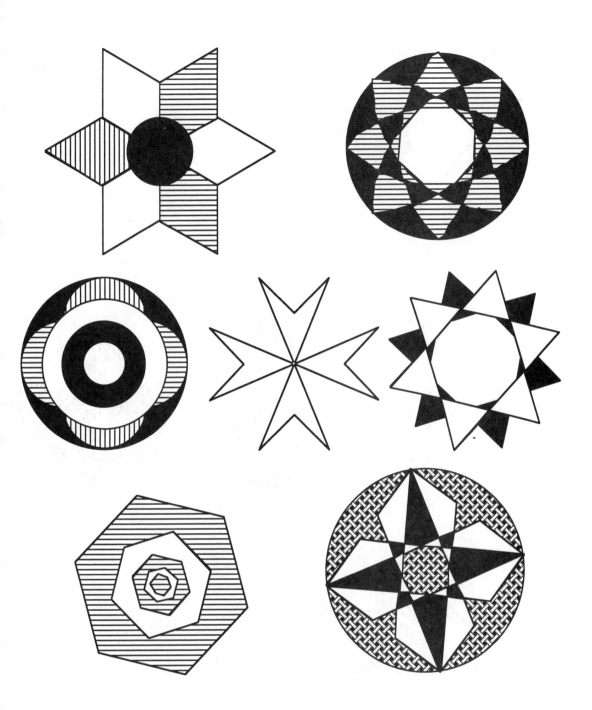

GLOSSARY

absolute value: (| |) The distance of a number from zero on the number line. It is always non-negative. (53)

acute angle: An angle with a measure greater than 0° and less than 90°.

acute triangle: A triangle with all three angle measures less than 90°.

addition: (+) An operation that tells how many objects there are when two sets are combined. The result is the number of objects in the two sets together, called a sum. In arithmetic, the word "object" usually means "number." (49)

adjacent angles: Angles which share a common side and vertex but no common interior points.

algebra: A branch of mathematics that uses variables to generalize the rules of numbers and numerical operations.

algebraic expression: Variables and constants, joined by addition or subtraction. Examples: 3x or 2x + 4 (129)

algorithm: A fixed rule for carrying out a mathematical procedure. Example: To find the average of a set of values, find their sum and divide by the number of values.

altitude of a triangle (height): The perpendicular distance from a vertex to the opposite side (or its extension) of a triangle.

angle: A geometric figure made up of two rays or line segments that have the same endpoint.

angle bisector: A ray that divides an angle into two congruent parts. (409)

arc: The portion of a circle between two points on a circle. (408)

area: The measure in square units of the interior region of a plane figure or the surface of a three-dimensional figure. (156)

area of a triangle: To find the area of a triangle, multiply the length of the base (b) by the height (h) and divide by two. $A = \frac{1}{2}bh$ (221)

area of a circle: $A = \pi r^2$, where r is the length of the radius of the circle. See area. (225)

associative property for addition: Changing the grouping of the numbers does not change the result in addition. Example: $(5 + 3) + 7 = 5 + (3 + 7)$ (402)

associative property for multiplication: Changing the grouping of the numbers does not change the result in multiplication. Example: $(5 \cdot 3) \cdot 2 = 5 \cdot (3 \cdot 2)$ (402)

average (mean): The sum of given numbers divided by the number of numbers used in computing the sum. Example: The average of 1, 4, and 10 is $(1 + 4 + 10) \div 3 = 5$. (14)

axis (pl. axes): A number line which can be used to indicate a position of a point, based on its coordinates. (28)

base of an exponent: The number used as the factor in an exponential expression. Example: $5^2 = 5 \cdot 5$. The number 5 is the base. (298)

415

base: For a triangle, the base may be any side, although usually it is the bottom one. For a trapezoid the two parallel sides are the bases. For a cylinder or prism, either one of the two congruent parallel faces may be the base while for a pyramid or cone, the base is the (flat) face which does not contain the vertex (where all the sides come together). (215, 221, 309)

bimodal: A set of numbers that has two modes. (18)

box-and-whisker plot: A graphic way of showing a summary of data using the median, quartiles, and extremes of the data. (27)

certainty: When an event will definitely happen. The probability of a certain event is 1.

center: (or center point) The point equidistant from all points on a circle. (407)

central angle: An angle whose vertex is the center of a circle. (410)

chord: A line segment that connects two points on a circle. (410)

circle: The set of all points in two dimensions that are the same distance r from a fixed point P. The fixed point P is called the center of the circle and the distance r is called the radius. (222)

circumference: The distance around the outside of a circle. You can calculate circumference from the diameter (d) or the radius (r). $C = \pi d = 2\pi r$. (225)

coefficient (numerical): The numeral part of a term, such as 6 in 6x. (260)

combining like terms: When working with an expression, terms that are exactly the same except for their coefficients can be combined into one quantity. Terms are combined by addition and subtraction of the coefficients. Example: $3x^2 + 2y + 6 + 4y - 2x^2 = x^2 + 6y + 6$. (141)

common: Shared. (159)

common factor: A common term factor: (1) in arithmetic, the integers multiplied are called factors; (2) in algebra, a monomial or polynomial that is a factor of a polynomial. For example: $10x + 15 = 5(2x + 3)$. Five is the common factor. (159)

common multiple: A number that is a multiple of the two or more numbers. Example: 24 and 48 are common multiples of 3 and 8. (86)

commutative property: The property of an operation such that changing the order of the numbers does not change the result of the operation. Examples: $3 \cdot 4 = 4 \cdot 3$ or $7 + 8 = 8 + 7$

compass and straightedge (construction with): A geometric construction. The straightedge is only used to draw line segments. The compass is used to transfer equal distances and draw arcs and circles. (407)

complementary angles: Two angles whose sum is 90°.

complementary probabilities: Two probabilities are complementary if their sum is one.

complex fraction: A fraction with a fraction in the numerator and/or the denominator.

composite figure: A shape made of several simpler figures.

composite number: A number with more than two factors.

compound interest: Interest paid on both the principal and previous interest earned which accumulates over time. It can be calculated by using the formula $B = p(1 + r)^t$, where B is the balance, p is the principal, r is the annual rate, and t is the time in years the account earns interest. (265)

cone: A three dimensional figure with one circular base and one vertex. (375)

congruent: Figures which have the same size and shape. (207)

conjecture: An educated guess based on data, patterns, and data. Scientists use the term hypothesis.

consecutive: In order. Example: 8, 9,10 are consecutive numbers. (10)

constant: A numerical term which does not change.

coordinate: See ordered pair.

coordinate grid (system): A two dimensional system formed by two perpendicular number lines that intersect at their zero points. The location of a point is given by first stating the horizontal location (x) and then the vertical location (y), written as an ordered pair, (x, y). (28)

correlation: A measure of interdependence of two sets of data. (33)

corresponding parts: Points, edges (sides), or angles in congruent or similar figures that are arranged in similar ways. For instance if ∆ABC is similar to ∆DEF, then side AB corresponds to side DE and angle C corresponds to angle F. (229)

cross multiplication: A way to find a missing numerator or denominator in equivalent fractions by multiplying diagonally across the equal sign to get an equivalent equation without fractions.
Example: In $\frac{a}{b} = \frac{c}{d}$, after cross multiplication the equation would be ad = bc. (212)

cube: A rectangular prism with 6 congruent faces, all squares.

cubic unit: A cube each of whose edges measures 1 unit in length. Volume is measured in cubic units. (293)

cylinder: Commonly, a three dimensional object with two circular, congruent, and parallel bases. (319)

decimal point: The dot separating the ones and tenths places in a decimal number.

denominator: The lower part of a fraction which tells into how many equal parts the whole is divided. (108)

dependent events: Two events are dependent if the outcome of the first event affects the outcome of the second event.

diagonal: A segment that joins two vertices of a polygon and is not one of the sides.

diameter: A line segment that has its endpoints on the circle and passes through the center. The longest chord in a circle. (222)

difference: The answer to a subtraction problem. (58)

digit: One of the ten numerals: 0, 1, 2, 3, 4, 5, 6, 7, 8, 9.

distributive property: For any a, b, and c, a(b + c) = ab + ac.
Example: $10(7 + 2) = 10 \cdot 7 + 10 \cdot 2$ (159)

dividend: A quantity to be divided. See divisor.

divisible: A number is divisible by another if their remainder is zero.

division: The inverse operation to multiplication. The operation which creates equal groups. (75)

divisor: The quantity by which another quantity is to be divided. dividend ÷ divisor = quotient (26

dodecagon: A polygon with 12 sides. (411)

edge: The line segment where two faces of a solid figure meet. (369)

endpoint: Either of the two points which mark the ends of a line segment. (409)

enlargement ratio: The ratio of similarity comparing a figure to a similar larger one is often called the enlargement ratio. This number tells you by what factor the first figure is enlarged to get the second.

equal: Having the same value.

equal ratios: Two equivalent fractions; a proportion. (208)

equation: A mathematical sentence relating two mathematical expressions with an equal sign (=). (173)

equilateral triangle: A triangle with all three sides the same length. (408)

equivalent: Naming the same amount with a different name. (91)

evaluate (an expression): To evaluate an expression, substitute the value(s) given for the variable(s) and perform the operations according to the order of operations. (129)

even number: A whole number which is divisible by two with no remainder.

event: One or more results of an experiment.

exponent: In the expression 2^5, 5 is called the exponent. The exponent indicates how many times t use the base as a multiplier. (298)

expression: See algebraic expression.

face: A flat side of a three-dimensional figure. (309)

factor: When two or more numbers are multiplied, each of the numbers multiplied is a factor of the product. (158)

factored form: The result of writing an algebraic expression as a product.
Example: $4x^3 + 12x^2 + 8x = 4x(x + 1)(x + 2)$ (137)

formula: An equation that shows a mathematical relationship. (279)

fraction: A number expressed in the form $\frac{a}{b}$ where a and b are integers and b is not equal to 0. (4)

frequency: The number of times something occurs in an interval or in a data set.

graph: A visual display of information in an organized manner. (6)

greatest common factor (GCF): The largest number which will divide evenly into two or more numbers. Example: 6 is the greatest common factor of 12 and 18.

guess and check table: A problem solving strategy in which you begin by making a guess and then check whether or not your answer is correct. In the process of checking, you gain information about how close your guess might be and make adjustments to your guess. Being organized is crucial to the success of this method, as well as writing a usable table. Guess and check leads to writing equations to represent word problems. (15)

height (altitude): The perpendicular distance between two bases, or between a vertex and a base. See altitude. (215)

hexagon: A polygon with six sides. (411)

horizontal: Parallel to the horizon. The x-axis in a coordinate grid is the horizontal axis. (45)

hypotenuse: In a right triangle, the longest side of the triangle, opposite the right angle, is called the hypotenuse. (291)

identity property of addition: Zero is the identity for addition. It does not change the value of a number when added to the number. (401)

identity property of multiplication: One is the identity element for multiplication. Multiplying by one does not change the value of a number. (93)

impossibility: An event with a probability of zero.

independent events: Two events are independent if the outcome of the second event does not depend on the outcome of the first event.

inequality: A mathematical sentence which compares two quantities, showing they are not the same. The symbols used may be: < (less than), > (greater than), to), or ≠ (not equal to). (69)

integers: The set of numbers { . . .,-3, -2, -1, 0, 1, 2, 3,... } (49)

intersect: To meet or cross. The intersection of two sets consists of all the points or elements that belong to both sets.

interval: A set of numbers between two given numbers.

inverse operations: An operation that undoes another operation. Example: Multiplication is the inverse operation for division. (295)

irrational numbers: Numbers that cannot be written as the ratio of two integers. (225)

isosceles triangle: A triangle with at least two sides equal in length.

least common multiple (LCM): The smallest common multiple of set of two or more numbers. Example: The least common multiple of 4 and 6 is 12. (86)

leg of a right triangle: Either of the two shorter sides of a right triangle. (291)

like terms: Terms that have the same variable part and corresponding exponent. 5 and 19 are like terms, 3xy and 5xy are like terms, $6x^2$ and $-3x^2$ are like terms. (141)

line: An infinite set of points forming a straight path extending in two directions. (12)

line segment: A part of a line between two endpoints. (407)

linear equation: An equation whose graph is a line, generated by an equation with a linear expression in it. (344)

linear expression: An expression in the form of ax + b, where a and b are numbers.

literal equation: An equation with two or more variables. (250)

lower quartile: The median of the lower half of an ordered set of data is the lower quartile. (27)

lowest common denominator (LCD): The smallest common multiple of the denominators of two or more fractions. Example: The LCD of $\frac{5}{12}$ and $\frac{3}{8}$ is 24.

mean: A measure of central tendency often referred to as the average. See average. (26)

measure of central tendency: Mean, median, and mode are all measures of central tendency, reflecting specific statistical information about a set of data. (26)

median: The middle number of a set of ordered data. If there is no distinct middle, the average of the two middle numbers is the median. (26)

midpoint: The point on a line segment that divides the line segment into two congruent line segments. (409)

mixed number (fraction): A number with an integer component and a fraction component. Example: $2\frac{3}{4}$ (199)

mode: The number or numbers that occur the most often in a set of data. There can be more than one mode. (26)

multiple: The product of a whole number and any other (nonzero) whole number. Example: 15 is a multiple of 5.

multiplication: An operation which reflects repeated addition. Example: $3 \cdot 4 = 4 + 4 + 4$. (71)

natural numbers: The counting numbers beginning with one. Example: 1, 2, 3... (49)

negative correlation: A relationship between two sets of variables in which one generally increases as the other decreases. (33)

negative numbers: Numbers which are less than zero, designated with a $-$ sign. (49)

negative slope: Lines that slant downward from left to right showing a negative ratio when comparing the vertical change to the horizontal change. (339)

net: A two dimensional one-piece plan which can be folded into a three dimensional shape. (321)

non-linear: A set of points which do not lie on a straight line when connected.

number line: A diagram representing all real numbers as points on a line. (12)

numeral: An expression (which is not a variable) that names a particular number.

numerator: The number above the bar in a fraction which tells the number of parts in relationship to the number of parts in the whole. (91)

obtuse angle: An angle whose measure is greater than 90° and less than 180°.

octagon: A polygon with eight sides. (411)

odd number: An integer which cannot be evenly divided by two. (34)

operation: In mathematics, addition, subtraction, multiplication, division, raising to a power and taking a root are operations.

order of operations: Rules which define in what sequence operations will be completed when an expression is presented for evaluation. Expressions inside parentheses are evaluated first, then multiplication or division (left to right) followed by addition and subtraction (left to right). Exponents are a form of multiplication. (131)

origin: The point assigned to zero on the number line or the point where the x- and y-axes intersect in a coordinate system. (28)

ordered pair: A pair of numbers (a, b) used to indicate a position on a coordinate plane. The first number indicates the horizontal coordinate; the second number indicates the vertical coordinate. Syn: coordinate. (28)

outcome: Possible result in an experiment or consequence of an action. (85)

outlier: A number in a set of data that is much larger or much smaller than the other numbers in the set. (14)

parabola: A graph of the equation $y = ax^2 + bx + c$ with $a \neq$ zero. (79)

parallel: ($\parallel$) Two straight lines on a two-dimensional surface which never intersect and are the same distance apart are said to be parallel. (215)

parallelogram: A quadrilateral with opposite sides parallel. (215)

pentagon: A polygon with five sides.

percent: (%) A ratio that compares a number to 100. (119)

perfect square: The product of an integer times itself gives a perfect square. Examples: 1, 4, and 9 are perfect squares because $1 = 1 \cdot 1$; $4 = 2 \cdot 2$; $9 = 3 \cdot 3$; $16 = 4 \cdot 4$... (298).

perimeter: The distance around a figure on a flat surface. (11)

perpendicular: (⊥) Lines, segments, or rays that intersect to form right angles.

perpendicular bisector: A line, ray, or segment that divides a segment into two congruent segments and is perpendicular to the segment. (409)

pi (π): The ratio of a circle's circumference to its diameter. An irrational number, it is common to use the approximation of 3.14 or $\frac{22}{7}$ if you are not using a scientific calculator with a π key. (223)

place value: The value of a position of a digit in a number.

plane: A flat surface that extends infinitely in all directions. It has no thickness.

point: An exact location in space. In two dimensions, an ordered pair specifies a point in a coordinate plane. (28)

polygon: A two-dimensional closed figure made of straight line segments (sides or edges) connected end to end (at vertices). The segments may not cross. Examples: triangle or quadrilateral. (309)

polyhedron: A three-dimensional figure with no holes in which all faces are polygons.

population: A collection of objects or group of people about whom information is gathered.

positive correlation: A relationship between two sets of variables in which one generally increases as the other increases. (33)

positive slope: Lines that slant upwards from left to right showing a positive ratio when comparing the vertical change to the horizontal change of the line. (339)

positive numbers: Numbers that are greater than zero.

power (exponent): See exponent.

prime: A number with exactly two factors. Examples: 2, 3, 5, 7...

prime factorization: The expression of a number as the product of prime factors.

prism: A three-dimensional figure composed of polygonal faces and two parallel, congruent faces called bases. No holes are permitted in the solid. The remaining faces are parallelograms (or rectangles). A prism is named for the shape of its base. (309)

probability: The chance of an event happening. When the outcomes are equally likely, it equals the number of event outcomes divided by the total number of outcomes. Example: when rolling a number cube, the probability that you will roll a 3 is: $\frac{1 \text{ way}}{6 \text{ possible outcomes}} = \frac{1}{6}$. (85)

product (·): Result of multiplying. Example: 72 is the product of 8 · 9. (71)

proportion: An equation of two equivalent ratios. Example: $\frac{1}{3} = \frac{3}{9}$ (208)

pyramid: A polyhedron with a polygonal base and whose other faces are triangles with a common vertex. A pyramid is named for the shape of its base.

Pythagorean Theorem: The sum of the squares of the lengths of the legs of a right triangle is equal to the square of the length of the hypotenuse. (294)

quadrants: The four sections of a coordinate grid. (46)

quadrilateral: A polygon with four sides.

quartile: Along with the median, the quartiles divide a set of data into four groups of the same size. (27)

quotient: The result of a division problem. (74)

radius: (plural: **radii**) The distance from the center to a point on the circle. (225)

random sample: A sample in which each item in the population or sample space has an equal chance of being selected.

range: In statistics, the difference between the least and greatest values in the data set. (14)

rate: A ratio comparing two quantities, often a comparison of time. Example: miles per hour. (337)

rate of change: see slope (337)

ratio: A comparison of two numbers which can indicate division. It can be written three ways: 2 boys to 5 girls, 2 boys : 5 girls, or $\frac{2 \text{ boys}}{5 \text{ girls}}$. (207)

ratio of similarity: The ratio of similarity between any two similar figures is the ratio of any pair of corresponding sides. In this course ratios will always be listed in the order that compares the "new" to the "original" figure. This ratio is also known as the enlargement or reduction factor in this course. (233)

rational number: A number that can be written in the form $\frac{a}{b}$ with a and b integers and $b \neq$ zero.

ray: A portion of a line that has one endpoint and extends forever in one direction.

real numbers: The set of rational and irrational numbers. (All the numbers on the number line.)

reciprocals: Two numbers which have a product of 1. Example: 2 and $\frac{1}{2}$ are reciprocals of each other. (256)

rectangle: A quadrilateral with four right angles. Its two pairs of opposite sides are parallel and congruent. (11)

reduce: To put a fraction into simplest form. (99)

regular polygon: A polygon in which all sides are congruent and all angles have the same measure.

representative sample: A subset (group) of a given population with the same characteristics as the population.

rhombus: A quadrilateral with four congruent sides.

right angle: An angle whose measure is 90°. (291)

right triangle: A triangle with one right angle in it. (291)

root: A number that can be used as a factor a given number of times. Example: The square root of 16 is 4 because $4 \cdot 4 = 16$. $\sqrt{16} = 4$ (298)

scale factor: A ratio between two sets of measurements. (229)

scale (scaling): An arrangement of numbers in uniform intervals. (12)

scalene triangle: A triangle with no two sides of equal length.

scatter plot: Two related sets of data graphed as points, often in a coordinate plane. See positive and negative correlation. (30)

scientific notation: A method of writing very large or very small numbers as a product of a power of ten and a number greater than or equal to one and less than 10. Example: $124,500 = 1.245 \cdot 10^5$ (386)

sector: A part of the interior of a circle bounded by two radii and the arc between their endpoints.

semi-circle: Half of a circle.

set: A collection of items. (313)

similar figures: Figures which are similar have the same shape but not necessarily the same size. The lengths of the corresponding sides are proportional to one another; the corresponding angles are congruent. (229)

simple interest: Interest paid only on the principal (the amount invested). It is found by multiplying the principal, the rate, and the time in years. (265)

simplest form of a fraction: A fraction whose numerator and denominator have no common factor greater than one. (99)

simplify: To combine like terms; to express the quantity using as few symbols as possible; to put a fraction in lowest terms. (99, 106)

slope: A way to specify the steepness of a line defined as the ratio of the vertical distance divided by the horizontal distance between any two points on the line. (339)

solution: Any value for a variable that makes an equation true. (176)

square: A quadrilateral with four congruent sides and four right angles. (410)

square number: Any number which is the product of two identical integers.
Examples: $1 \cdot 1 = 1$, $2 \cdot 2 = 4$, $3 \cdot 3 = 9$ ... (298)

square root: See root.

square measure: The units used to describe the measure of an area in the form of 1 x 1 unit squares. (293)

stem and leaf plot: A frequency distribution made by arranging the data. (19)

straight angle: An angle whose measure is 180°.

subproblems: A problem solving strategy which breaks a problem into smaller parts which must be solved in order to solve the original, complex problem. (304)

substitution: Replacing one symbol by another (a number, a variable, or other algebraic expression) without changing the value of the expression.

subtraction (-): An operation that gives the difference between two numbers. (57)

sum: An answer to a addition problem. (49)

supplementary angles: Two angles whose measurements give a sum of 180°.

surface area: The total area of all faces and bases of a polyhedron, cylinder, cone, or pyramid. (315)

term: Each part of the expression separated by addition or subtraction signs is a term. (131)

tetrahedron: A polyhedron with four faces.

tick mark: An indicator that a number line has been divided into intervals of equal length. (46)

trimodal: A set of data that has three modes. (18)

truncate: To cut off or shorten.

trapezoid: A quadrilateral with exactly one pair of parallel sides. (221)

triangle: A polygon with three sides. (221)

unit price: The cost of one item or one measure of an item. Example: cost for one pound or one gallon.

unit rate: A rate with a denominator of one.

units digit: The numeral in the ones place.

upper quartile: The median of the upper half of an ordered set of data. (140)

variable: A symbol or letter that represents a number. (140)

vertex: The point at which two rays, line segments, or lines meet.

vertical: At right angles to the horizon. In a coordinate grid, the y-axis runs vertically. (45)

vertical angles: The angles opposite each other when two lines intersect.

volume: The number of cubic units inside a three dimensional object. (311)

x-axis: The horizontal number line on a coordinate grid. (28)

x-intercepts: The point(s) where a graph intersects the x-axis. An x-intercept always has coordinates (x, 0). (54)

y-axis: The vertical number line on a coordinate grid. (28)

y-intercepts: The point(s) where a graph intersects the y-axis. The y-intercept always has coordinates (0, y). (54)

INDEX

Chapter Prefixes

Many of the page numbers listed here contain the definitions or examples of the topic listed. It may be necessary, however, to read text on preceding pages or the pages following to understand the topic fully. Also, on some page numbers listed here you will find "good examples" of the topic, but they may not offer any explanation. It is very important, therefore, for you to be sure you correct and complete your homework and keep it organized. Your record of the problems related to these topics may be your best index to understanding the mathematics of this course.